BIOLOGY *first*

WITHDRAWN

BIOLOGY *first*

George Bethell

David Coppock

OXFORD

UNIVERSITY PRESS

OXFORD
UNIVERSITY PRESS

Great Clarendon Street, Oxford OX2 6DP

Oxford University Press is a department of the University of Oxford.
It furthers the University's objective of excellence in research, scholarship,
and education by publishing worldwide in
Oxford New York

Auckland Cape Town Dar es Salaam Hong Kong Karachi
Kuala Lumpur Madrid Melbourne Mexico City Nairobi
New Delhi Shanghai Taipei Toronto

With offices in

Argentina Austria Brazil Chile Czech Republic France Greece
Guatemala Hungary Italy Japan Poland Portugal Singapore
South Korea Switzerland Thailand Turkey Ukraine Vietnam

Oxford is a registered trade mark of Oxford University Press
in the UK and in certain other countries

© George Bethell and David Coppock 1999
The moral rights of the authors have been asserted
Database right Oxford University Press (maker)

First published 1999
10 9 8 7

British Library Cataloguing in Publication Data
Data available

ISBN : 978-0-19-914731-1

Typeset by Ian Foulis and Associates, Plymouth, Devon
Printed in China

Acknowledgements

The publishers would like to thank the following for providing
photographs:

8 (top left) **FLPA/ Roger Wilmshurst**, 8 (top right) **FLPA/ E. & D.
Hosking**, 8 (bottom left) **FLPA/ Tony Wharton**, 8 (bottom right) **SPL/ Dr
Kari Lounatmaa**, 9 (top left) **FLPA/ Silvestris**, 9 (top centre) **OSF/ Len
Rue**, 9 (top right) **FLPA/ F. Polking**, 9 (bottom left) **Stock Market/ T. & D.
McCarthy**, 9 (bottom centre) **FLPA/ H. Hautala**, 9 (bottom right) **OSF/
Richard Packwood**, 9 (lower right) **FLPA/ F. de Nooyer/ Foto Natura**, 10
(top left) **SPL/ E. Grave**, 10 (bottom left) **SPL/ J. Walsh**, 10 (top right) **SPL/
M. Abbey**, 11 (top left) **SPL/ Biophoto Associates**, 11 (top right) **SPL/
NIBSC**, 11 (bottom left) **SPL/ Claude Nurisdany & Marie Perennov**, 11
(bottom right) **SPL/ Andrew Syred**, 11 (lower right) **SPL/ Gene Cox**, 13
(top) **Heather Angel**, 13 (bottom) **OSF/ B. Watts**, 15 **SPL**, 16 (top)
Colorsport, 16 (bottom) **Colorsport**, 17 **Peter Gould**, 18 **Camera Press**,
19 (top) **SPL/ Dr J. Burgess**, 19 (bottom) **Camera Press**, 20 (left) **David
Coppock**, 20 (right) **David Coppock**, 21 (top) **J. Allan Cash**, 21 (bottom)
Peter Gould, 23 (top) **OSF/ Alastair Shay**, 23 (centre) **OSF/ Waina Cheng**,
23 (bottom) **OSF/ Peter Parks**, 27 (top left) **SPL/ Jeremy Wachter**, 27 (top
centre) **FLPA/ Silvestris**, 27 (top right) **FLPA/ Lee Rue**, 27 (bottom left)
FLPA/ Ray Bird, 27 (bottom centre) **FLPA/ Silvestris**, 27 (bottom right)
FLPA/ H. B. Brandl, 31 (both) **Peter Gould**, 33 (top) **SPL/ Dr J. Burgess**,
33 (bottom) **OUP Library**, 34 (top) **Peter Gould**, 34 (bottom) **Bruce
Coleman**, 36 **David Coppock**, 40 (top) **Health Education Council**, 40
(bottom) **Zefa**, 41 (left) **OSF/ London Scientific Films**, 41 (centre) **SPL/
Michael Abbey**, 41 (right) **OUP Library**, 44 (top) **The Sunday Times/ Ian
Yeomans**, 44 (centre) **National Medical Slide Bank**, 44 (bottom) **SPL/
Michael Abbey**, 46 (top) **SPL/ Petit Format**, 46 (centre) **SPL/ Petit
Format**, 46 (bottom) **SPL/ Petit Format**, 47 **SPL/ Carolyn Jones**, 49 (all)
OUP Library, 57 (left) **SPL/ National Cancer Institute**, 57 (right) **SPL/
Dr T. Brain**, 59 (top left) **FLPA/ Roger Wilmshurst**, 59 (top centre) **SPL/
David Nunuk**, 59 (top right) **FLPA/ L. Batten**, 59 (bottom left) **FLPA/ Paul
Hart**, 59 (bottom centre) **FLPA/ A. Wharton**, 59 (bottom right) **SPL/ F. S.
Westmorland**, 63 (top) **Zefa/ Hinz**, 63 (bottom) **Zefa/ Dr Baer**, 64 **OSF/ B.
Watts**, 68 **OSF/ David Boag**, 69 **David Coppock**, 71 **David Coppock**, 73
(top left) **Heather Angel**, 73 (top centre) **David Coppock**, 73 (top right)

Peter Gould, 73 (centre) **Peter Gould**, 73 (bottom) **Peter Gould**, 74 **Peter
Gould**, 76 **Stock Market/ Chuck Savage**, 77 (all) **Peter Gould**, 78
Geoscience Features, 79 (left) **Stock Market/ Steve Prezant**, 79 (right)
Stock Market/ Ronnie Kaufman, 81 (top) **J. Allan Cash**, 81 (bottom) **SPL/
Michael Abbey**, 82 (top) **Bruce Coleman**, 82 (bottom) **J. Allan Cash**, 83
(top) **Hulton Picture Library**, 83 (centre) **Hulton Picture Library**, 83
(bottom) **OSF/ J. Cooke**, 84 (top left) **Zefa**, 84 (bottom left) **Zefa/ W.
Hamilton**, 84 (centre) **Bruce Coleman**, 84 (top right) **Zefa**, 84 (centre right)
Bruce Coleman, 84 (bottom right) **Laurie Morton**, 85 (top) **Heather
Angel**, 85 (bottom) **J. Allan Cash**, 89 (left) **Mike Roberts**, 89 (right) **Laurie
Morton**, 90 (top left) **Stock Market/ Pete Saloutos**, 90 (top right) **FLPA/
Celtic P.A.** , 90 (bottom left) **FLPA/ J. Hutchings**, 90 (bottom right) **FLPA/
John Hawkins**, 91 **OSF/ Press-Tige**, 93 (left) **Holt Studios**, 93 (right) **Holt
Studios**, 94 (top) **FLPA/ Fritz Polking**, 94 (bottom) **OSF/ M. Wilding**, 99
(all) **Chris Honeywell**, 100 (top) **FLPA/ Roger Wilmshurst**, 100 (bottom)
FLPA/ K. Delport, 101 **Dr Terry Jennings**, 104 **Chris Honeywell**, 105
OSF/ John Downer, 106 (top) **OSF/ John Downer**, 106 (bottom) **Bruce
Coleman**, 108 **OSF/ W. Johnson**, 110 **SPL/ Dr Jeremy Burgess**, 111 (top
right) **SPL/ Pekka Parvianen**, 111 (centre left) **FLPA/ M. B. Withers**, 111
(centre middle) **FLPA/ E. & D. Hosking**, 111 (centre right) **FLPA/
Silvestris**, 111 (bottom left) **SPL/ Crown Copyright/ Health and Safety
Laboratory**, 111 (bottom centre) **Stock Market**, 111 (bottom right) **FLPA/
T. Montford/ Foto Natura**, 112 (top left) **SPL/ David Parker**, 112 (top
centre) **FLPA/ Ray Bird**, 112 (top right) **SPL/ BSIP Krassovsky**, 112
(centre middle) **OSF/ Ian West**, 112 (centre right) **FLPA/ W. Broadhurst**,
112 (bottom centre) **OSF/ Ronald Toms**, 112 (bottom right) **SPL/ Martin
Bond**, 114 (left) **SPL/ Hank Morgan**, 114 (top right) **SPL/ Tektoff**, 114
(centre) **SPL/ Dr Tony Brain**, 114 (bottom right) **SPL/ Dr A. Lesk**, 115
Chris Honeywell, 119 **Holt Studios/ Nigel Cattlin**.

The artwork is by: Brian Beckett, Elitta Fell, Ian Foulis Associates, David La
Grange, Nick Hawken, Oxford Illustrators, Jones Sewell, Alan Rowe, Julie
Tolliday, and Galina Zolfaghari.

Introduction

Biology is the study of the living world around us. It covers everything, from what goes on inside the bodies of animals and plants, to the natural environments where they live and upon which they rely for food and shelter. This huge scale makes biology exciting, but it is also a very practical subject. As you will see, modern technologies such as biotechnology and microbiology are based on applications of biology.

This book has been written for students, like you, studying biology in secondary schools. It covers all the life processes and information about living things that you need for Key Stage 3 of the National Curriculum. However, in many places it goes into much greater depth, helping you to develop the kind of understanding needed to gain the highest grades in your SATs. It will also provide a solid foundation if you are preparing for GCSE.

There are six chapters, covering many important topics, particularly those that affect our everyday lives. Topics are presented over two or four pages, and there are lots of diagrams and photographs to help you. There are also questions and activities to check that you have understood the main ideas. Each chapter finishes with a page of questions to help you test your knowledge and to prepare for examinations. Of course, biology is more than just learning from books, however good they are, and your school's programme of practical work will help you to develop important experimental skills.

To get the most out of this book:

- use the contents page to find out where the major topics are covered;
- use the index to find the pages where you can read about particular key words;
- use the questions within the chapter to test your knowledge as you go;
- carry out the activities suggested to reinforce your understanding;
- use the questions at the end of each chapter to prepare for tests and examinations.

We hope that you will enjoy using this book and finish it feeling confident that you can use the ideas and methods of biology to understand the way our living world works.

George Bethell

David Coppock

Contents

1 Life and living things

What is biology?
What are cells?
What are organisms?
How much energy is there in food?
How can we use fermentation?
Who's related to whom?

The things in these pictures may look very different to each other, but they all have one significant thing in common – they are all **alive**.

Living things can be identified because they have certain characteristics. They all carry out the same **life processes**, although they don't all do these in exactly the same way. A cat moves very quickly when it chases a mouse. An ivy plant, on the other hand, moves very slowly as it grows up a wall towards the light.

Biologists try to find out more about life and living things by studying animals and plants and in particular, the way they behave.

Biology is the study of living things.

Life processes

All living things have seven characteristic features or life processes.

Animals **move** by using their legs, wings or fins. Plants move by growing towards or away from something.

Living things need energy to grow, to move and to enable the body to work properly. Energy is released from food in a process called **respiration**.

Animals **feed** to produce energy and to grow. They eat other living things. Plants make their own food by photosynthesis.

All living things produce waste such as carbon dioxide, urine and faeces. The removal of waste from the body is called **excretion**.

Animals only **grow** until they reach a certain height. Plants, however, grow continuously all through their lives.

Animals use sense organs such as eyes and ears to **respond** to what is going on. Plants do not have sense organs but can still react to things such as light and water.

All living things must **reproduce** to replace those that die. Asexual reproduction does not involve sex. Most animals and plants have male or female sex organs. They use sexual reproduction to produce young.

Questions

1 Suggest why an animal needs to move quickly.

2 Why do we eat food?

3 What use is made of the energy released in respiration?

4 What do plants excrete?

5 What is the difference between asexual and sexual reproduction?

6 A car moves, takes in fuel, releases energy from fuel and gets rid of waste through the exhaust pipe. Is a car a living thing? Explain your answer.

Cells: the building blocks of life

What is a cell?

A cell is a unit of living material. **All** living things are made up of one or more cells.

The amoeba shown here is an animal made of only one cell. Plants and animals with just one cell are called **unicellular** organisms.

Multicellular organisms are made up of a number of cells. Human beings are multicellular and have millions of cells.

Plant and animal cells have similar jobs to do. They take in food, release energy, get rid of waste, grow and reproduce. Their structures, however, are not the same.

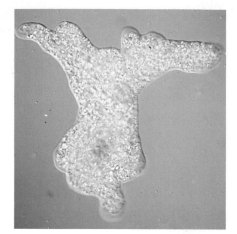

Amoeba

Cell structure

This is a photograph of some animal cells. These are cheek cells from the lining of someone's mouth. They have been stained to make them clearer to see.

These plant cells come from the leaf of a pond weed.

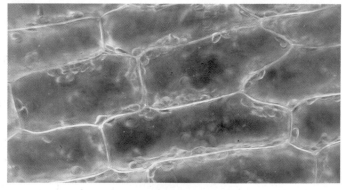

The main parts of the animal cell are shown in the diagram below.

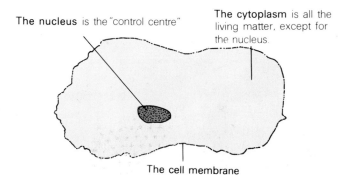

The nucleus is the "control centre"

The cytoplasm is all the living matter, except for the nucleus.

The cell membrane

The main parts of the plant cell are shown in this diagram.

The cell wall is a rigid (firm) coating round the outside of the cell. It helps the plant cell to keep its shape

nucleus

The cell membrane is inside the cell wall

cytoplasm

The vacuole is a large space filled with a liquid called cell sap

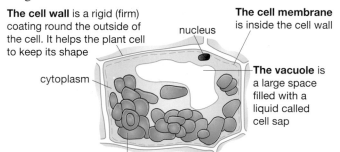

Chloroplasts contain the green chemical called chlorophyll. This is the chemical which allows green plants to use the sun's light energy

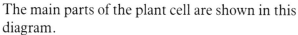

Questions

1 Why are cells sometimes called the 'building blocks of life'?

2 Why do you need a microscope to see a unicellular organism?

3 List **three** similarities between plant and animals cells.
List **three** differences between plant and animal cells.

4 Why were the cheek cells in the photograph above coloured with a dye?

From cells to organisms

Humans and other multicellular organisms are made up of different types of cell. Each type of cell or group of cells carries out a different job. As a result cells from a plant or animal may not all look the same. Some cells are designed:

. . . to carry messages . . .

Nerve cells have long thin fibres to carry electrical impulses over long distances through the body.

. . . to carry chemicals . . .

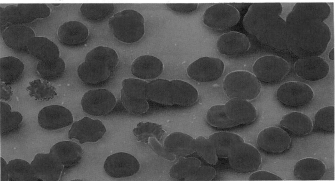

These red blood cells carry oxygen around the body. They have a large surface area to pick up lots of oxygen.

. . . to absorb water . . .

These cells from the root of a plant absorb water from the soil. They increase the surface area of the roots.

. . . to provide protection.

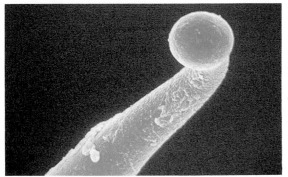

This is the sting cell of a nettle. It is very sharp and produces an irritating chemical.

Specialized cells together make **tissues**. Muscle tissue is made of cells whose job it is to contract and cause body movement. Skin and bone are also tissues.

Various tissues together make an **organ**. An organ performs important jobs in the body. The heart is the organ responsible for blood circulation.

Organs work together to form **organ systems**. The digestive system is an example; it is made up of various different organs such as the stomach and intestines.

An **organism** is a plant or animal which can exist on its own. It is made up of organ systems which work together to carry out all the functions of a living thing.

Questions

1   Name some of the organs in your body.

2   List the tissues that make up one of these organs.

3   What is the difference between an organ and an organ system?

4   Why do you think cells are so specialized in complex animals and plants?

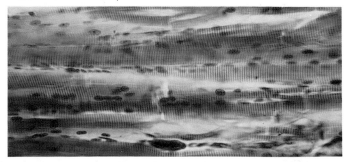

Muscle tissue

Organ systems

As you will have read on page 11, many organs work together in groups called organ systems.

Organ systems carry out much larger jobs in the body than a single organ is able to.

Some of the main organ systems of the human body are shown below.

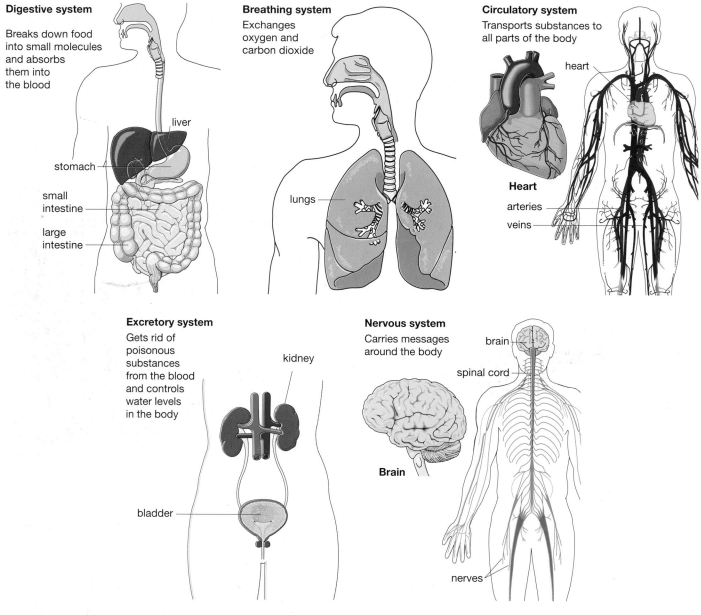

Digestive system

Breaks down food into small molecules and absorbs them into the blood

liver

stomach

small intestine

large intestine

Breathing system

Exchanges oxygen and carbon dioxide

lungs

Circulatory system

Transports substances to all parts of the body

heart

Heart

arteries

veins

Excretory system

Gets rid of poisonous substances from the blood and controls water levels in the body

kidney

bladder

Nervous system

Carries messages around the body

brain

spinal cord

Brain

nerves

Questions

1 What is the job of the:
   a) breathing system?
   b) circulatory system?
   c) excretory system?
   d) nervous system?
   e) digestive system?

2 Turn to page 45 and look at the diagrams of the human reproductive organs.
   a) Name *two* organs that make up the female reproductive organs, and *two* organs that make up the male reproductive organs.
   b) What is the job of the reproductive organs?

Sex cells and life cycles

Most animals and plants have cells in their body which are very different from any others. These cells are sex cells or **gametes**. Their job is to pass on information from one generation to the next.

Gametes are made in sex organs. In animals the male sex cells are **sperms** which are made in the **testes**. The female gametes are **eggs** and these come from the **ovaries**. Sperms are much smaller than eggs and, unlike eggs, are able to move on their own. They consist of a 'head' containing a large nucleus and a long tail which wiggles to propel the sperm along.

Egg cells are less complicated than sperms. A large nucleus is surrounded by cytoplasm which in some animals, particularly birds, contains yolk. The yolk provides food for the young animal as it grows in the egg. Human eggs have no yolk, a human baby obtains its food from its mother while in the womb.

In all animals, sexual reproduction involves the fusion of a sperm nucleus with an egg nucleus. The method by which sperms and egg are brought together, however, may be different.

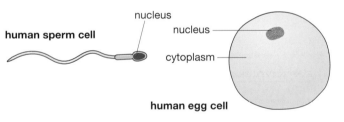

Human sex cells or gametes

In humans and other mammals fertilization and development of the young takes place inside the female.

Life cycles

A life cycle describes the stages in development of members of a species from fertilization of one generation to fertilization of the next. The life cycle of humans and most other animals follows the pattern shown.

Mating reptiles

In reptiles and birds fertilization is internal, eggs are laid and the young develop outside the mother's body.

The male frogs sits on the female's back. He produces sperm as she lays her eggs.

In most fish and amphibians fertilization and development of the young takes place outside the body of the female.

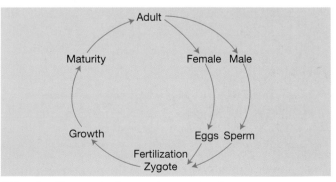

Life cycle of humans (and most other organisms)

13

Respiration: it's all about energy

Carbohydrates and fats are high-energy food substances. Digestion breaks these down into simpler molecules such as glucose. It is the energy holding these simple molecules together that is released during the process of respiration.

We can summarize aerobic respiration in a chemical equation:

glucose + oxygen → carbon dioxide + water + ENERGY

$$C_6H_{12}O_6 + 6O_2 \rightarrow 6CO_2 + 6H_2O + 2880\,kJ$$

If you have studied fuels you may notice that this form of respiration is very similar to burning a fuel. We can use this fact to measure the energy stored in different types of food.

Measuring the amount of energy stored in food

As the food, in this case sugar, burns it releases heat energy. This heat passes into the water causing the temperature to rise. The more energy in the food, the higher the temperature of the water will go. The table shows the results for sugar, a peanut and some dried bread.

table of results	sugar	peanut	dried bread
vol of water in test tube	50 ml	50 ml	50 ml
mass of water	50 g	50 g	50 g
mass of food	1 g	1 g	1 g
temp of water at start	21 °C	21 °C	21 °C
temp of water at finish	71 °C	91 °C	51 °C
temp rise	50 °C	70 °C	30 °C

By using this formula it is possible to calculate the amount of energy (in joules) in the food).

$$\text{energy} = \frac{\text{mass of water (in grams)} \times 4.2 \times \text{temperature rise (in °C)}}{\text{mass of food (in grams)}}$$

For example:

$$\text{energy in sugar} = \frac{50\,g \times 4.2\,J/°C \times 50\,°C}{1\,g}$$

$$= \mathbf{10\,500\,J \text{ or } 10.5\,kJ}$$

Now calculate the energy value of the peanut and the dried bread.

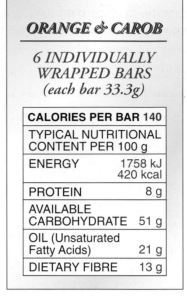

ORANGE & CAROB	
6 INDIVIDUALLY WRAPPED BARS (each bar 33.3g)	
CALORIES PER BAR 140	
TYPICAL NUTRITIONAL CONTENT PER 100 g	
ENERGY	1758 kJ 420 kcal
PROTEIN	8 g
AVAILABLE CARBOHYDRATE	51 g
OIL (Unsaturated Fatty Acids)	21 g
DIETARY FIBRE	13 g

Nutritional value tables include energy values.

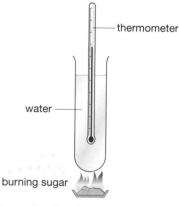

Energy from burning sugar

Activities

1 The experiment described gives us a rough idea of the energy value of foods. However, the number of joules calculated is *not* very accurate.

a) Suggest why the result is not very accurate. Give at least three reasons.

b) Design a better apparatus for this experiment. Draw a labelled diagram of your idea.

2 The energy value of food is often given on the packet.

Find the energy value in kilojoules (kJ) of the following foods:

a) a chocolate bar ('Mars' or similar)

b) baked beans

c) tinned fruit in syrup

d) breakfast cereal

Which one has the most energy in each gram? (You may need a calculator!)

Respiration in cells

Respiration is often confused with breathing. This is because breathing is sometimes called **external respiration**. External respiration is the exchange of gases between an animal or plant and the surrounding air.

Respiration should strictly be called **tissue respiration**, because it takes place in the cells of body tissue.

Tissue respiration is the process by which energy is released from the chemical breakdown of glucose. You will have seen on page 14 that glucose is the fuel for the chemical reaction of respiration. This reaction occurs in every living cell in tiny rod-shaped structures called **mitochondria**. These are very small: the photograph shown opposite was taken using an electron microscope. The mitochondria have been enlarged 24 000 times.

Mitochondria are found in the cytoplasm of all cells, but the number varies. Muscle cells, for example, have lots of mitochondria because they have to release large amounts of energy quickly for movement.

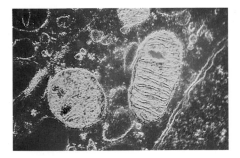

The mitochondria in this cell are where respiration takes place.

Storing energy

The energy released during respiration is needed for many things. We need it for movement and to keep our body temperature steady. As a result it is very important that our bodies should be able to store energy, as chemical energy, ready for use.

For **long-term** storage the body uses **fat** molecules, but these cannot be broken down quickly. Cells must store energy for quick release when necessary. They do this by using a chemical called **ATP**. (The letters stand for **a**denosine **trip**hosphate. It is a complicated molecule that has *three* phosphate groups attached to it.)

The chemical bond holding the second and third phosphate groups together is a **high-energy bond**. When it is broken a new molecule, ADP (adenosine diphosphate), is formed and energy is released.

ATP is a **short-term** energy store in the cells, which can release energy quickly when needed.

When the cell has excess energy, ADP molecules and phosphate groups can be joined to make ATP again.

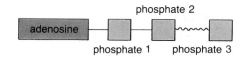

Model of an ATP molecule

Questions

1 What is the difference between external respiration and tissue respiration?

2 **a)** What are mitochondria?
  b) Where are they found in cells?

3 Explain why muscle cells have more mitochondria than bone cells.

4 Why do muscle cells need a short-term energy store?

Energy without oxygen (1): in animals

Most living cells in both plants and animals respire aerobically. That is, they use oxygen in the release of energy from food substances. However, sometimes an animal's breathing rate cannot get oxygen to the cells quickly enough. For example, if you are running a race you may create an oxygen shortage in your cells. (You may have heard sports commentators refer to this as an 'oxygen debt'.) Your muscles need to release more energy for movement but oxygen cannot get to the cells fast enough. So, where does the energy come from under these conditions?

ATP seems like the obvious answer but unfortunately ATP is only a short-term energy store and it is quickly used up. The body must therefore 'borrow' some energy from glucose in its cells. It does this by breaking the glucose down, without oxygen, into a substance called **lactic acid**. Lactic acid is a sort of halfway stage between glucose and its breakdown products, carbon dioxide and water. Energy is released and so you can continue running.

However, lactic acid builds up in the muscle cells causing muscle fatigue and eventually painful **cramp** – it all depends upon how fit you are!

Athletes need to release energy quickly.

After the exercise (or when cramp has forced you to stop) you usually gasp for air taking in lots of oxygen, your heart will also be beating faster to get more oxygen to the cells.

The lactic acid is slowly converted into carbon dioxide and water releasing more energy which is used to rebuild ATP molecules.

The process can be summarized as follows:

$$C_6H_{12}O_6 \rightarrow 2C_3H_6O_3 + 150\,kJ$$
$$\text{glucose} \qquad \text{lactic acid} \quad \text{energy}$$

Since the process brings about the release of energy from food without oxygen it is called **anaerobic respiration**.

Questions

1 What is the main difference between aerobic and anaerobic respiration?

2 Explain why a person creates an oxygen shortage (debt) during vigorous exercise.

3 Why is lactic acid called an 'intermediate' breakdown product of glucose?

4 What is cramp and how is it caused?

5 Explain how the body gets rid of excess lactic acid.

6 Footballers sometimes get cramp, particularly during a long hard game. When the trainer comes on to the field he can often be seen rubbing the footballer's legs vigorously. Suggest how this action helps overcome cramp.

After the race oxygen is needed for recovery!

Energy without oxygen (2): in plants

Plant cells, like animals cells, can produce energy by anaerobic respiration if necessary. This time however, the intermediate product is not lactic acid but an alcohol called ethanol. The following equation summarizes the process:

$$\text{glucose} \rightarrow \text{ethanol} + \text{carbon dioxide} + \text{energy}$$
$$C_6H_{12}O_6 \qquad 2C_2H_5OH \qquad 2CO_2 \qquad 210\,\text{kJ}$$

Germinating seeds and plant roots living in water-logged soil can respire without oxygen for a short time. However, the plant must return to aerobic respiration before the level of ethanol in the cells becomes too high, otherwise it will die.

Yeast, a microscopic fungus, can respire anaerobically or aerobically, depending on oxygen levels.

When little or no oxygen is present yeast breaks down glucose into ethanol and carbon dioxide with the release of energy; a process commonly known as **fermentation**. The yeast uses the energy to live.

Fermentation has been used for many hundreds of years in both brewing and baking. In brewing it is the alcohol that is used in beers, wines and spirits. In baking the carbon dioxide produced in fermentation makes bread dough rise.

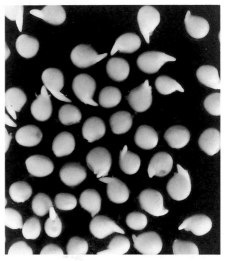

Germinating seeds can respire without oxygen.

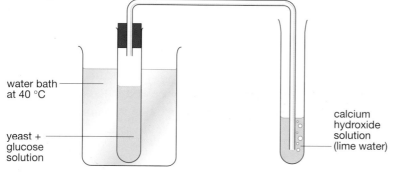

Investigating fermentation

Alcoholic fermentation in yeast

If some yeast is mixed with glucose solution and put in a warm place it will begin to ferment. A suitable apparatus for observing fermentation is shown in the diagram.

As the yeast breaks down the glucose to release energy a colourless gas is produced. This gas turns calcium hydroxide solution (limewater) milky.

What is this gas?

If the temperature of the water in the water bath is lowered by adding ice cubes, fewer bubbles of gas are produced. However, if the water temperature is raised to about 90 °C no bubbles are produced at all.

What effect do high temperatures have upon alcoholic fermentation in yeast?

Questions

1 A house plant needed watering once a week. When its owner went on holiday a 'kind' neighbour watered it once a day for two weeks. Explain why the plant died.

2 What is yeast? What does yeast produce when it respires anaerobically?

3 Yoghurt contains living bacteria. Bacteria are also capable of anaerobic respiration. If a sealed carton of yoghurt is left for a long time the lid bulges upwards. Suggest why this happens.

4 When yeast is used to make bread, the dough should be left in a warm place so that the yeast can produce carbon dioxide to make it rise. Explain why the dough would not rise if it were put straight into a hot oven.

5 Why is the amount of energy produced during fermentation much less than that produced by aerobic respiration?

Carbohydrates: the energy foods

Carbohydrates are food substances which can be used in the body to release energy. All carbohydrates contain carbon, hydrogen and oxygen atoms. Examples are the sugars, glucose ($C_6H_{12}O_6$) and maltose ($C_{12}H_{22}O_{11}$), and starch. The starch molecule has hundreds of sugar molecules joined together.

Sugars

Glucose is one of the simplest sugars. Its formula is $C_6H_{12}O_6$ and it has the ring shape shown in the diagram. There are other sugar molecules with this formula but their atoms are arranged differently. Fructose and galactose are two examples.

Sugars provide energy . . . but can cause tooth decay.

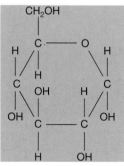

A glucose molecule

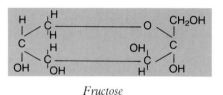

Fructose

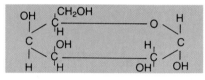

Galactose

Glucose, fructose and galactose are called single sugars or **monosaccharides**. They all have slightly different properties but they all taste sweet.

Two single sugar molecules can be linked together to form a double sugar or **disaccharide**. Maltose is a double sugar made when two glucose molecules join up with the loss of a water molecule. Reactions like this in which water is removed are called **condensation reactions**.

$$\text{glucose} + \text{glucose} \rightarrow \text{maltose} + \text{water}$$
$$C_6H_{12}O_6 + C_6H_{12}O_6 \rightarrow C_{12}H_{22}O_{11} + H_2O$$

Maltose, sucrose and lactose are all disaccharides. These also taste sweet.

Sugars in food

All sugars taste sweet and because people like the taste we use a lot in our food and drink.

Sugars are also soluble in water. This enables the dissolved sugar to be carried in the transport systems of animals and plants.

Unfortunately, sugar on our teeth encourages plaque and so causes tooth decay.

Many foods now carry lists of what they contain. If you look at the labels you may be surprised at some of the foods that have sugar added to them; these baked beans for example.

Questions

1 Look at the diagrams of the glucose and fructose molecules.
  a) List *two* similarities between them.
  b) List *one* difference between them.

2 Why are glucose and fructose called 'carbohydrates'?

INGREDIENTS		
Beans, Tomato Purée, Water, Sugar (2.2 %), Salt (0.5 %), Modified Starch, Onion Powder, Spices		

NUTRITION

A serving = approx. ⅓ of the can.

AVERAGE COMPOSITION	PER 140 g (5 oz) serving	PER 100 g (3 oz) serving
Energy	353 kJ/84 kcal	252 kJ/60 kcal
Fat	0.6 g	0.4 g
Protein	7.0 g	5.0 g
Available Carbohydrate	13.3 g	9.5 g
Fibre	10.2 g	7.3 g
Added Salt	0.7 g	0.5 g
Added Sugars	3.0 g	2.2 g

Even baked beans contain sugar!

Starch: a big carbohydrate molecule

We have seen how two glucose molecules can be joined to give a maltose molecule. The two monosaccharides join to give a disaccharide. In fact many single sugar molecules can join together in condensation reactions. The larger sugar molecules formed are called **polysaccharides**.

Starch is a polysaccharide with several hundred condensed glucose molecules linked together in a chain. Its formula is written as $(C_6H_{10}O_5)_n$ where n is the number of glucose 'building blocks' linked together.

These plant cells contain grains of starch.

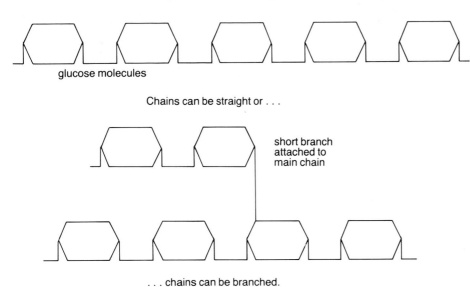

glucose molecules

Chains can be straight or . . .

short branch attached to main chain

. . . chains can be branched.

Starch does not dissolve in water. Because it is insoluble it can be used as a way of storing glucose. In plants the starch molecule chains are folded and bundled together to form starch grains like the ones shown in the photograph at the top of the page. Starch grains are found in large numbers in rice, wheat and other cereal crops, all of which are grown for food. The starch stored in animals is a little different to that found in plant cells. Animal starch is called **glycogen**.

Rice has a high starch content.

Questions

1 What is the difference between a monosaccharide, disaccharide and a polysaccharide?

2 What are the building blocks of starch molecules?

3 **a)** Give two differences between starch and glucose.
   b) Give one similarity between starch and glucose.

4 Write the formula for a starch molecule that is made of 500 glucose molecules.

5 Starch is found in plants and animals as a food store.
   a) What makes starch molecules ideal as a food store?
   b) Name two foods that we eat that contain a lot of starch.
   c) Why do we eat starchy foods?
   d) What happens if we eat too many starchy foods?

Fermentation

This is fermentation on a very large scale.

This bakery produces about 500 000 loaves of bread a week.

This brewery produces over 54 000 000 litres of lager a week.

Bakers add yeast to dough to make it rise. The yeast feeds on the sugars in the dough and as it respires it produces carbon dioxide. The gas forms bubbles in the dough because it cannot escape. These are the holes that you can see in baked bread. During baking the yeast is killed and fermentation stops.

In wine and beer making it is the other by-product of fermentation, alcohol, which is required. Wine is made as yeast feeds on the sugars in fruit. The type of wine produced depends upon the type of fruit used. Most commercial wine is made from grapes.

Beer and lagers are made from barley. Barley seeds are allowed to germinate until all the seed food stores are converted into sugar. The sugar is in fact maltose (often referred to as 'malt'). Boiling water is then added which stops germination and dissolves the sugar. Yeast is mixed into this sugar solution and the mixture is allowed to ferment. Flavourings are added to beers to produce different varieties. For example, hops give bitter beer its distinctive taste.

Spirits such as whisky, gin and brandy are made from wine or the sugar from germinating barley. Brandy is made by distilling wine, whisky comes from the distillation of fermented maltose solution. Since yeast cannot live in high concentrations of alcohol, wines and beers have a limited strength (maximum 20 per cent alcohol). Distillation provides a means of extracting nearly all of the alcohol produced during fermentation. Spirits are much stronger than wine.

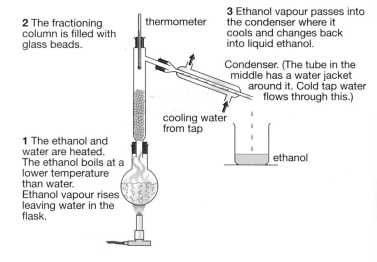

2 The fractioning column is filled with glass beads.

thermometer

3 Ethanol vapour passes into the condenser where it cools and changes back into liquid ethanol.

Condenser. (The tube in the middle has a water jacket around it. Cold tap water flows through this.)

cooling water from tap

1 The ethanol and water are heated. The ethanol boils at a lower temperature than water. Ethanol vapour rises leaving water in the flask.

ethanol

Distillation of ethanol

Questions

1 What do you suppose happens to the alcohol produced by the yeast during the making of bread?

2 When making some wines extra sugar must be added to the fruit and yeast mixture. Why should this be necessary?

3 Scottish malt whisky is world famous. How do you think it got its name?

4 Describe how brandy is made.

Alcohol the drug

A small amount of alcohol makes people feel happy and relaxed but alcohol is really a **depressant** drug. It depresses or reduces brain activity and thereby affects judgement, self control and the time taken to react to a stimulus.

The level of alcohol in the blood is measured in milligrams per 100 millilitres of blood (mg/100 ml). Drinking a single unit of alcohol raises the concentration of alcohol in the blood by about 15 mg/100 ml.

The legal driving limit for blood alcohol level is 80 mg/100 ml but even when at this level a driver is three times more likely to have an accident than if they had not drunk at all. The only really safe limit when driving is no alcohol at all! Drunken driving is a major cause of road accidents. One third of drivers killed in such accidents have blood alcohol levels well in excess of the legal limit.

Drunken driving is a major cause of road accidents. One third of drivers killed in accidents have blood alcohol levels above the legal limit.

Questions

1 a) How many pints of beer would a person need to drink to be over the legal limit?
b) Why would a small person need to drink less alcohol than a large person to be over the limit?

2 a) How many glasses of wine would a person need to drink to be over the legal limit?
b) Explain why *two* glasses of wine at lunchtime and *two* pints of beer on the way home from work could put a driver over the legal limit.

Like many other drugs alcohol can be **addictive**. However, unlike other addictive drugs it is available in supermarkets, off-licences and pubs. Therefore people need to be careful about how much alcohol they drink otherwise they may become dependent; they become alcoholics. Alcoholics, like other drug addicts, run a great risk of serious damage to their health. It is a sad reflection on our society that more and more young people are becoming hooked on alcohol.

*These drinks contain the same amount of alcohol – this is called **one unit**.*

Consider the following facts:

- too much alcohol present in the blood over a number of years can lead to liver damage. **Hepatitis** (liver inflammation) and **cirrhosis** (scarring of liver tissue) are common amongst heavy drinkers and can cause death.

- some people often go without food and have a drink instead. These people are likely to develop stomach ulcers and other problems in the digestive system.

- a high blood alcohol level causes a rise in blood pressure. High blood pressure can be a contributory factor in cases of coronary heart disease.

It is in everyone's interest to either avoid alcohol or to drink within sensible limits.

Questions

1 What is an 'alcoholic'?

2 How may alcohol damage the body of an alcoholic?

3 People with high-pressure jobs often drink alcohol at lunchtime without eating food. Why is this dangerous?

4 Explain why it is illegal for a shopkeeper or a publican to sell alcohol to a person under 18 years of age.

5 Suggest ways of reducing the number of school students who drink alcohol.

Classifying organisms

Imagine how difficult it would be to find a particular book in a library if the thousands of books were scattered all over the place in no logical order. If libraries didn't have systems of classification none of us would ever find the book we were looking for.

In the same way, no one can ever hope to know the names of all the living organisms found on Earth. Scientists have therefore devised a classification system for all known living things. Organisms are sorted into groups on the basis of features that they have in common.

Grouping together

The **species** is the smallest classification group. Members of a species can breed together to produce fertile offspring.

Similar species are grouped into **genera** (singular: **genus**). All members of a genus have common features. For example, the domestic cat, *Felis domestica*, the lynx, *Felis lynx*, and the mountain lion, *Felis concolor*, belong to the same genus, *Felis*.

The classification system continues by grouping related genera into **families**. The cat family, Felidae, includes the domestic cat, the lion (*Panthera leo*), and the cheetah (*Acinonyx jubatus*).

A group of similar families is called an **order**. Cats, dogs (Canidae), bears (Ursidae), and weasels (Mustelidae) are all from the order Carnivora.

Orders with common features are grouped into **classes**. The order Carnivora belongs to a most important class, the Mammalia, which includes bats, monkeys, horses, whales, kangaroos, apes, and humans.

Classes are grouped into **phyla** (singular: **phylum**). Mammals are members of the phylum Chordata which contains all the animals with a spinal cord. Fish, amphibians, reptiles, and birds are also chordates.

The biggest groups of all are the **kingdoms**. The Chordates, along with the Arthropoda and Mollusca, belong to the **Animal Kingdom**. Other kingdoms include the **Plant Kingdom** and the **Kingdom Fungi**.

Scientific names

Organisms have a scientific name in addition to a common name. An organism must have a name which refers to it and it alone, and is understood all over the world. For example, in North America the names puma, cougar, and mountain lion all refer to the same animal. By using the single scientific name, *Felis concolor*, any possible confusion is avoided.

The modern system of classification is based on the work of the Swedish naturalist, Carl von Linné (1707–78). He gave every known plant and animal a Latin name and grouped together organisms according to their similar features. Latin was chosen because it was the international language of science. Linné even Latinized his own name to Carolus Linnaeus!

group	example (animal)	example (plant)
kingdom	Animal	Plant
phylum	Chordata	Angiospermae
class	Mammalia	Dicotyledons
order	Carnivora	Ranales
family	Canidae	Ranunculaceae
genus	*Canis*	*Ranunculus*
species	*familaris*	*bulbosus*
scientific name	*Canis familiaris* (domestic dog)	*Ranunculus bulbosus* (bulbous buttercup)

Levels of classification

Questions

1 Why is classification necessary?

2 Which is **a)** the largest **b)** the smallest classification group?

3 How many classes in the Animal Kingdom can you name?

   a) Why was Latin chosen for naming organisms?

   b) Explain why Latin names are useful.

5 Write a classification table like the above for **a)** the brown bear (*Ursus arctos*) **b)** the stoat (*Mustela erminea*).

For many years only two kingdoms were recognized, the plant and animal kingdoms. However, there are thousands of organisms, mostly very small, that are neither plant nor animal, or have both plant and animal features. These organisms are grouped separately from plants and animals. Today, many scientists recognize five kingdoms.

Kingdom Monera

Monera are living organisms which closely resemble the earliest forms of life on Earth. They live as single cells, or in colonies of identical cells. Their cells don't have a true nucleus. Instead, their genetic material (DNA) lies free in the cytoplasm, not enclosed by a nuclear membrane. Their cell walls are rigid, like plant cells, but they are made of materials not found in any other kingdom. Bacteria and blue–green algae are typical monerans. Over 3000 species are known.

Kingdom Protoctista

Protists are single-celled organisms living individually or in colonies. The kingdom is very varied having over 28 000 known species. The cells of protists have true nuclei. Genetic material is enclosed by a nuclear membrane. All protists live in water or moist places. Examples of protists are simple forms of algae and protozoa. Protozoa are sometimes called 'the first animals' because they feed by digesting complex food materials, just like us!

Kingdom Fungi

The **Fungi** form a large group of organisms made up of about 75 000 named species. For many years fungi were classified with plants, but are now recognized as a separate kingdom. Some fungi, like yeasts, live as single cells. Most, however, have a more complex structure – pin mould and the mushroom are good examples. The body of a fungus is made up of a **mycelium** (network) of thread-like **hyphae**. A hypha contains true nuclei and other typical cell structures but doesn't have cross walls to divide it up into individual cells. Fungi do not have chlorophyll and therefore cannot make food by photosynthesis. They feed by digesting their food outside themselves and then absorbing it.

Purple bacteria growing on seaweed

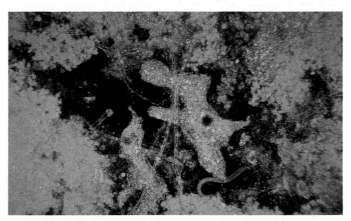

Amoeba (a protozoon) in pond debris

Fungi

Questions

1 What single feature would help you to identify a member of the Kingdom Monera?

2 Why are the protists sometimes called 'the first animals'?

3 Suggest two ways in which fungi differ from plants.

4 Explain why scientists today divide all known organisms into five kingdoms instead of two.

Who's related to whom? (2)

The Plant Kingdom

Most plants consist of more than one cell. In fact, they usually have many thousands of cells specialized into different tissues and systems. Plants have chlorophyll and make their own food by photosynthesis. Over 300 000 plant species have been listed. Plants are classified like this:

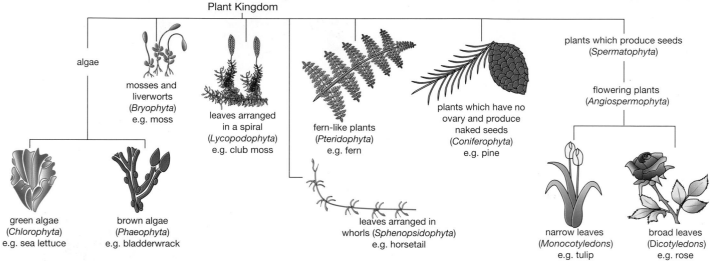

The Animal Kingdom

Animals are multicellular organisms whose cells have flexible cell membranes and no cell wall. Their cells are specialized into tissues, organs, and systems. Animals usually move to get their food, which is swallowed and digested inside the body. Of the 1.5 million listed animal species, over 1 million are insects. Animals are classified like this:

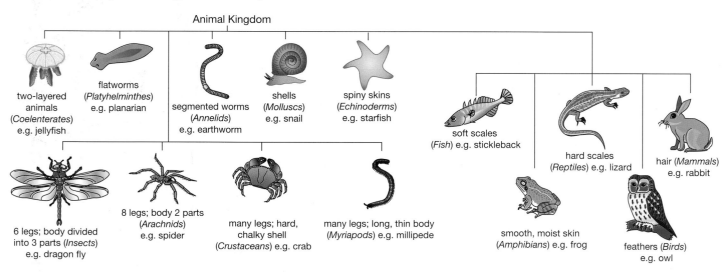

Questions

1 What classification group do:
   a) bluebells and primroses
   b) frogs, turtles, and rabbits belong to?

2 Give one feature that insects, crabs, spiders, and centipedes have in common.

3 Animals with jointed legs belong to the Phylum Arthropoda.
   a) How many classes are there in this phylum?
   b) Name them.

4 What is: a) the largest b) the smallest classification group shown in the above diagrams?

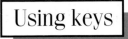

Using keys

What do we do when we want to know the name of an organism that we cannot recognize? The answer is to use a **key**. A key is a series of questions which we ask ourselves. Each answer leads on to another question. This goes on until eventually the name of the organism is found.

Here is a simple key which will help you to name the four 'unknown' animals shown opposite.

Question 1   Does the animal have flippers?
              Answer: Yes   **dolphin**
                         No   Go to question 2

Question 2   Does the animal have wings?
              Answer: Yes   **bat**
                         No   Go to question 3

Question 3   Does the animal have a bushy tail?
              Answer: Yes   **squirrel**
                         No   **otter**

Here is a different kind of key. It works in just the same way as the one above, but it is presented in the form of a flow chart. Use it to identify the wild flowers shown opposite.

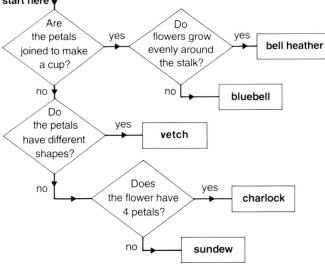

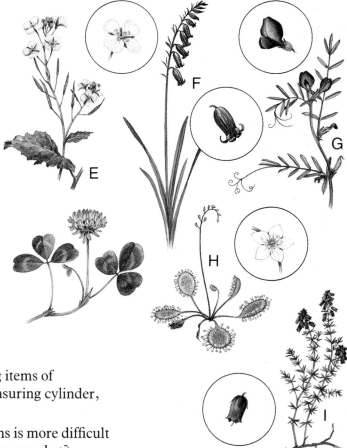

Questions

1   What are the names of organisms A–I on this page?

2   Why are keys useful?

3   Explain briefly how to use a key.

4   Make up a key to help someone identify the following items of laboratory glassware: beaker, test tube, filter funnel, measuring cylinder, conical flask.

5   Why do you think the classification of living organisms is more difficult than the classification of books in a library or food in a supermarket?

1 **a)** What is respiration?

b) The equation below represents one form of respiration.

$$C_6H_{12}O_6 + 6O_2 \rightarrow 6CO_2 + 6H_2O + ?$$
(Glucose)

i) Is this aerobic or anaerobic respiration?

ii) How do you know?

iii) Name the *two* products shown in the equation.

iv) What product does ? represent?

2 'In 1968 the Olympic games were held in Mexico City. This caused problems for long distance runners because at 2300 m above sea level the atmosphere is thin and contains less oxygen. Many athletes developed severe muscle cramps. Others had to be given pure oxygen to breathe after they collapsed.'

a) Why does the air in Mexico City 'contain less oxygen' than the air near sea level?

b) Why did the lack of oxygen cause runners to develop muscle cramps? (Your answer should include the terms *oxygen debt* and *lactic acid*.)

c) Suggest how breathing pure oxygen instead of air helps the athletes recover.

3 The label shown below is from a tin of pasta shapes.

CONSUMER CARE	
NUTRITION INFORMATION	
100 GRAMS OF THIS PRODUCT TYPICALLY PROVIDES	
12.0 grams of Protein	HIGH
75.0 grams of Carbohydrate	HIGH
2.0 grams of Fat	LOW
Energy value	·1480 kJ
(Calories)	(347 kcal)

a) Name *two* listed food substances which can provide energy.

b) Some of the carbohydrate is starch. Describe the structure of a starch molecule.

c) Why is starch useful in the body?

4 **a)** Describe the effects of alcohol on a person's reactions and general behaviour. Explain how these effects can make accidents more likely at work and in the street.

b) Alcohol is an addictive drug.

i) What is meant by 'addictive'?

ii) What laws do we have in our society to control drinking?

5 The diagram below shows some home made wine fermenting.

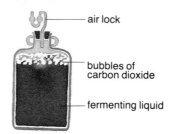
air lock

bubbles of carbon dioxide

fermenting liquid

The liquid contains fruit juice, sugar and yeast.

a) What is fermentation?

b) i) One of the products of fermentation is a colourless gas which bubbles out of the air lock. Name the gas.

ii) The other product is a colourless liquid which, when drunk, affects the nervous system. Name the liquid.

c) Most home wine makers know that fermentation is faster when the glass jar is kept in a warm cupboard. However, an impatient wine maker decides to heat up the fermenting liquid until it boils. Why doesn't he get his wine?

6 This label is from a bottle of whisky.

WHITE TREES

OLD SCOTCH

WHISKY

DISTILLED USING THE FINEST QUALITY BARLEY GRAINS

43% VOL

a) Describe how the whisky was made.

b) The bottle contains 1000 ml (1 litre) of whisky. 43 per cent is alcohol.

i) Calculate the volume of alcohol in the bottle.

ii) 10 ml of alcohol has a mass of about 7 g. Estimate the mass of the alcohol in the bottle.

iii) The average body contains about 5000 ml of blood. The legal limit for driving is 80 mg of alcohol in 100 ml of blood.

Show that someone who drinks half a bottle of whisky is way over the limit.

What gives the body its shape?
How do animals move?
How do animals get information about their surroundings?
How do animals reproduce?
How do animals stay healthy?

These animals all need to work hard to keep their bodies healthy. Of course, there are lots of differences between them. For a start, they are not all the same kind, some have hair and some do not, some are big and some are small. However, their bodies work in exactly the same way. They all need to eat food, they can all move quickly if necessary, and they can all catch diseases.

It is important to study how the bodies of animals work. We can use the information to prevent illness and to control the spread of disease.

By keeping healthy, humans and other animals can lead long and enjoyable lives.

Activities

1 Describe two of the animals in the photographs. You could consider hair colour, length of hair, number of legs, tail or no tail, position of eyes, and many other things.

2 Describe five ways a group of ten sixteen-year-olds might vary. Consider factors such as height and body mass.

3 How can exercise alter the appearance and health of an average person?

The human machine

Human beings, like most large animals, have a **skeleton** inside their bodies. A skeleton is a system of bones and other supporting material and has three important functions:

- it gives support to the rest of the body – like the framework of a building. This gives the body its shape.
- it gives protection to important and delicate organs of the body, for example, the skull protects the brain.
- it provides an anchorage for muscles. Muscles fixed to the skeleton can operate **joints**. This makes parts of the skeleton move.

From the diagram of the skeleton, you can see how the skull gives the head its shape. The brain is protected by the bones of the skull. The eyes are protected by bony sockets. Muscles attached to the jaw allow us to eat and speak.

Bones

In the human skeleton there are over two hundred bones. Some are long, some short, some round, some flat, but all bones have the same basic structure.

As a baby develops inside its mother's womb some cells form a tough, flexible substance called **cartilage** (gristle). (You can feel cartilage in your ears and at the end of your nose.) Slowly much of the cartilage changes to bone. Bone is very hard and strong. It has to stand up to large forces. Large bones have a hollow shaft inside them which makes them lighter. This makes movement easier. The bone **marrow** within the shafts produces blood cells.

Bones have living parts and non-living parts. The living part makes the bones slightly flexible. This lets them absorb sudden shocks. The bones of old people have less living material and so they become **brittle** and break easily.

The non-living part of a bone makes it stiff (rigid) and gives it strength. This can be shown by putting a bone in a beaker of dilute hydrochloric acid. After a few days the bone can be taken out and washed. The bone is now quite floppy! The acid has dissolved away the non-living part of the bone.

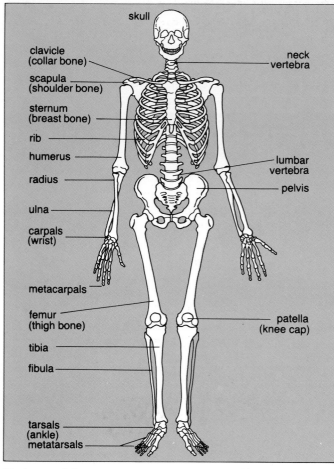

The human skeleton

Activities

1 Try to get a large, fresh bone from a butcher's shop. Don't forget to ask what animal it came from and what part of the skeleton it is.
 a) Draw the bone.
 b) Test the strength of the bone by trying to break it with your hands. (Do not try to smash it with a hammer; splinters of bone may injure you.)
 c) Get someone to cut the bone in half for you using a saw. Draw the inside of the bone. Is the bone hollow? Does it contain marrow?

2 If you have a chicken or turkey for dinner investigate the skeleton.
 a) Find and draw the large, flat bone at the centre of the bird's skeleton. (The large muscles of the wings were fixed to this.)
 b) Find the ribs. What do these protect in the living bird?
 c) Which features help the leg joints to function?

Moving the machine

The place where two bones meet is called a **joint**. Most of the joints in the body are movable. There are a number of different types. Each one produces a different kind of movement.

Joints are held together by **ligaments**. These are flexible and elastic to allow the joint to move, but strong enough to stop the joint coming apart. When a joint comes apart we say it is **dislocated**. The surfaces of the ends of bones are covered in smooth cartilage and the whole joint is filled with a liquid. This liquid, called **synovial fluid**, acts as a lubricant. The cartilage and the synovial fluid reduce friction and allow smooth movements. Large or uneven strain on joints can damage the cartilage layer. Sportsmen and women need to be careful to avoid sharp, sudden changes of direction if they wish to keep their joints healthy.

Muscles move bones at joints so that the individual bones act as levers. Muscles are attached by **tendons** to bones on either side of a joint. One end is usually attached to a bone which does not move. The other end is attached to a movable bone. When muscles **contract** they get shorter. This gives a pulling force. When the muscles relax they go back to their normal length but they cannot 'push'. Therefore at joints, muscles are arranged in pairs. One muscle of the pair pulls the joint one way and the other pulls it back again. Because the muscles work against each other they are called **antagonistic pairs**.

The human forearm is a good example. The biceps (flexor muscle) bend the arm and the triceps (extensor muscle) straighten the arm.

Questions

1 What is a joint?

2 Why are ligaments **a)** strong **b)** flexible?

3 What **two** features of a joint allow smooth movement?

4 Gymnasts sometimes suffer from 'dislocated shoulders'. What do you think this means?

5 Hockey players sometimes suffer from damaged cartilages in their knees. What do you think causes this?

6 What are antagonistic pairs of muscles?

7 Describe what happens to your muscles, joints and bones as you pick up a heavy box from the floor.

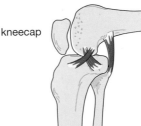

kneecap

Knee joint
This is a hinge joint. The bones can move in one direction only.

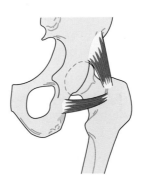

Hip joint
This is a ball-and-socket joint. The bones can move in almost any direction.

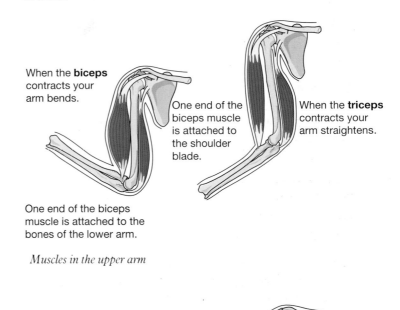

When the **biceps** contracts your arm bends.

One end of the biceps muscle is attached to the shoulder blade.

When the **triceps** contracts your arm straightens.

One end of the biceps muscle is attached to the bones of the lower arm.

Muscles in the upper arm

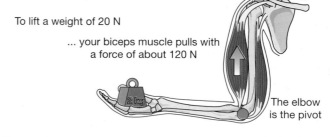

To lift a weight of 20 N

... your biceps muscle pulls with a force of about 120 N

The elbow is the pivot

Bones as levers

Keeping the machine going

Like all machines, the human body requires a constant supply of fuel and enough materials for repairs. The fuel for the human machine is **food**. Food supplies energy and all the chemicals needed for growth and to keep the body working properly.

Food types

The things we eat contain different types of food. The body needs these in the right quantities. If one type of food is missing, a person can become ill. On the other hand, too much can make a person unfit. For a healthy body you need a **balanced diet**. (See page 31.)

Carbohydrates are chemicals that supply energy. They include sugars, of which there are a number of types, and starch. Carbohydrates release energy when they are used up in cells. **Fats** are also energy foods. They provide more than twice the amount of energy than the same quantity of carbohydrates. A thin layer of fat under the skin acts as insulation and keeps the body warm. Too much fat is not healthy and does not make the body look good.

Proteins are needed to build new body tissues during growth. They are also used to repair damaged tissue. If you cut yourself new skin is made from protein.

Mineral salts are required only in small quantities. The human body needs a wide range of minerals. Calcium is important for the growth of bones and teeth. The haemoglobin (see page 41) in red blood cells contains iron. If you don't get enough iron in your diet, fewer red blood cells will be made. This condition is called **anaemia**. A person suffering from anaemia will look pale and feel tired.

Vitamins like mineral salts are also required only in tiny amounts. However, they play a vital part in the chemical reactions that take place in the body. If a vitamin is missing from your diet you will probably become very ill. Such an illness is called a **deficiency disease**. A deficiency of vitamin C causes scurvy, a disease that makes your gums swell and bleed, and slows down healing of wounds.

Water makes up the large proportion of our bodies. It is essential because all of the chemical reactions of the body take place in solution.

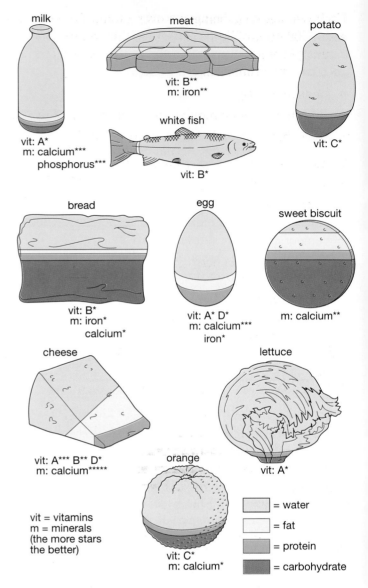

These diagrams show the proportions of carbohydrates, fats, proteins, vitamins and water in some foods.

Questions

1 Which food in the diagram above contains most:
a) carbohydrate **b)** fat **c)** protein **d)** water?

2 A cheese contains 2% carbohydrate, 28% fat and 25% protein. Draw a diagram to show this information.

3 Nearly half the school children in the United Kingdom are overweight. What kind of foods should these children avoid? Explain why.

4 Find out more about anaemia. What causes it? What effect does it have on the body? How can it be cured?

Healthy eating

Each year a human being eats over 1 tonne (1000 kg) of food and drinks about 500 litres of liquid! Not all of this will be good for maintaining a normal, healthy body. It is important to eat a varied diet – one which provides the right balance between:

● foods for energy
● foods that provide building materials and control chemical reactions
● foods that contain dietary fibre (roughage).

Getting the balance right is not always easy. Many of us just leave it to chance and eat what we like. However, it is clear that in Britain we eat far too much fat, sugar and salt. In addition, we do not eat enough fibre.

Energy foods

Fats and sugars are energy foods. Energy is measured in kilojoules (some people still refer to the old units – calories). The more kilojoules a food contains, the more energy it will provide. If you do not use up the available energy your body stores the excess food as fat and you will become overweight. At the moment about 30% of the adult population in Britain is overweight. Worse still, a lot of school pupils are overweight!

Proteins, vitamins, and mineral salts

Most people get more than enough protein, vitamins and minerals in their normal diet. The body cannot store proteins so eating more will not make you stronger or healthier than you already are. Strength and fitness will only come by carefully balancing healthy eating with exercise. If you are eating enough of the right kinds of foods then you are unlikely to be deficient in vitamins or minerals.

Unfortunately we do eat far too much common salt (sodium chloride). On average we consume about 12 g per day – we could do with half as much. Too much salt leads to high blood pressure so we ought to reduce the amount used in cooking and at the table. More and more food products are now labelled 'Low Salt' or 'No Salt Added' so we have the opportunity to cut down salt intake.

Fibre

Fibre or roughage is made up of the cell walls of plants which pass through the digestive system without being digested or absorbed. It adds bulk to the food giving the muscles in the walls of the digestive system something to push on. Foods containing a lot of fibre help prevent constipation and other disorders of the lower digestive tract such as haemorrhoids ('piles'). We should be eating about 30 g of fibre each day, on average we are only eating half that amount at the moment.

Food additives

Food additives should be listed and their function clearly explained on food packaging, for example, 'preservative – E200 (Sorbic acid)'.

Eating disorders

An eating disorder is the way some people find of dealing with troubled emotions and mixed-up feelings. There are three kinds of eating disorder.

Sufferers of **anorexia nervosa** believe they are overweight. They try to cut down the amount they eat, or avoid eating altogether to the point where they become dangerously underweight.

Bulimia nervosa describes people who go on an 'eating binge', consuming large amounts of food but then making themselves sick to get rid of it.

Complusive eaters also eat a lot of food, but don't try to get rid of it afterwards. They even eat without feeling hungry and usually become very overweight.

Roughage and carbohydrate foods

Protein, vitamins, and minerals

Digesting food

Only very small molecules of food can be absorbed by the body and pass into our blood system. Food, even after a lot of chewing, consists of very large molecules which cannot be dissolved. These must be broken down or **digested** into smaller, soluble molecules.

Digestion takes place in the digestive system and is brought about by the action of chemicals called **enzymes**.

The enzymes concerned with digestion are mixed with food at various points along the digestive system usually as part of digestive juices.

The digestive system

The gullet has muscles in its walls. These contract and relax to move food into the stomach. This process is called **peristalsis**. *Peristalsis enables you to swallow food even when you are standing on your head!*

In the stomach, food is mixed with **gastric juice** *which contains the enzyme* **pepsin**. *Pepsin begins the digestion of protein. Gastric juice also contains hydrochloric acid which kills the bacteria that are present in food. Continual mixing by the muscular stomach walls produces a creamy liquid which passes into the first part of the small intestine, the* **duodenum**.

Fat, protein and any starch which has not been digested in the mouth, is broken down in the duodenum. **Bile** *is a liquid made in the liver and stored in the gall bladder. It breaks down fats into tiny droplets to form an emulsion.*

The **pancreas** *produces a digestive juice which contains the enzymes that digest starch (amylase), fat (lipase) and protein (trypsin).*

Yet more enzymes are made in the walls of the small intestine. Their action brings about the complete breakdown of food molecules and the end of digestion.

Questions

1 Why must food be digested?

2 What two jobs are done by saliva?

3 Name *four* parts of our digestive system.

4 Explain what happens to
   a) a starch molecule
   b) a protein molecule
   as it passes through the digestive system.

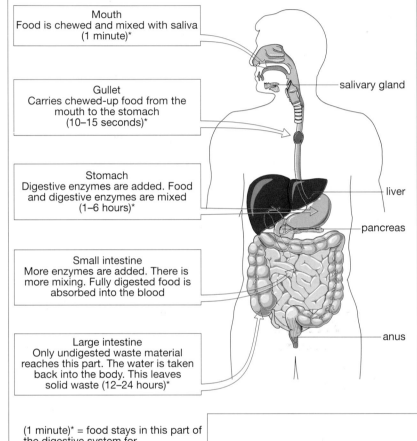

| Mouth |
| Food is chewed and mixed with saliva (1 minute)* |

| Gullet |
| Carries chewed-up food from the mouth to the stomach (10–15 seconds)* |

| Stomach |
| Digestive enzymes are added. Food and digestive enzymes are mixed (1–6 hours)* |

| Small intestine |
| More enzymes are added. There is more mixing. Fully digested food is absorbed into the blood |

| Large intestine |
| Only undigested waste material reaches this part. The water is taken back into the body. This leaves solid waste (12–24 hours)* |

(1 minute)* = food stays in this part of the digestive system for around 1 minute

salivary gland

liver

pancreas

anus

place	enzyme	food	product
mouth	salivary amylase	starch	maltose (sugar)
stomach	pepsin	protein	polypeptides (small proteins)
duodenum	amylase	starch	maltose
	lipase	fat	fatty acid + glycerol
	trypsin	protein	amino acids
small intestine	maltase	maltose	glucose
	lactase	lactose	glucose + galactose
	sucrase	sucrose	glucose + fructose
	lipase	fats	fatty acids + glycerol
	peptidase	peptides	amino acids

Enzymes

Enzymes are biological **catalysts**. This means they speed up a chemical reaction, but are not broken down or changed at the end. They lower the amount of energy required for chemical reactions (such as those that take place when food is digested) to take place.

How do enzymes work?

Enzymes are very specific. This means that they only work on one or two different types of molecule. The molecule that is broken down is called the **substrate**. Food molecules such as starch are substrates.

Research shows that enzymes work by firstly attaching themselves to substrate molecules.

The fit of the enzyme and the substrate must be exact, otherwise the enzyme will not do its job. This is often referred to as the lock and key mechanism, where the substrate 'key' must exactly fit the enzyme 'lock'.

The place on the enzyme molecule where the substrate fits is called an **active site**. A substrate molecule must stay attached to an enzyme at an active site until the substrate is broken down into smaller product molecules. The whole process is extremely quick if conditions such as temperature and pH are right.

enzyme + substrate → enzyme – substrate complex → enzyme + product molecules

Notice that once the enzyme has done its job, it is free to go on and catalyse the breakdown of more substrate molecules. This, together with the speed at which they work, is the reason why cells can function perfectly well with only a tiny amount of enzyme. (It is also the reason why you need only use a small amount of enzyme solution in enzyme experiments!)

Looking to see how enzymes speed up chemical reactions

Hydrogen peroxide (H_2O_2) breaks down into water and oxygen very slowly under normal conditions. If you put some hydrogen peroxide in a beaker you can see the oxygen being released as tiny bubbles. However, if a small piece of fresh liver is added to the hydrogen peroxide, see what happens. Fresh liver contains an enzyme. The breakdown of the hydrogen peroxide speeds up rapidly. How could you prove that the gas given off is oxygen?

Questions

1   The formula below shows the breakdown of hydrogen peroxide.
$$2H_2O_2 \rightarrow 2H_2O + O_2$$
   a) Name the two products of this reaction.
   b) A student finds that adding a small piece of fresh liver to some hydrogen peroxide in a test tube speeds up the release of oxygen. Design an experiment to find out whether the enzyme in the liver is sensitive to changes in pH.

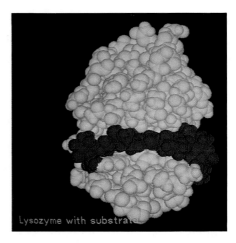

A model of the enzyme lysozyme showing the active site. Lysozyme is an enzyme found in tears. It kills bacteria by dissolving them! (The active site is in red.)

substrate molecule

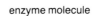

1 *Substrate 'key' moves into enzyme 'lock'*

enzyme molecule

2 *Substrate fits enzyme forming an enzyme-substrate complex*

product molecules

3 *Chemical bonds are broken and product molecules are released – the enzyme remains unchanged*

The result of adding a piece of liver to hydrogen peroxide.

Enzymes: what affects them

The activity of enzymes is affected by changes in acidity (pH) and temperature. Each enzyme works best at a particular level of pH and temperature. Its activity reduces above or below that point.

Pepsin is an enzyme found in the stomach. It helps in the digestion of protein and works most effectively at pH2 (strong acid). Trypsin is found in the duodenum and only functions in alkaline conditions (pH8).

Enzymes are actually proteins and they are affected by **heat**. Heat changes the structure of proteins. You can see this by watching what happens to the white of an egg when it is poached or fried. Our normal body temperature is 37°C and, not surprisingly, the enzymes in our cells work best at this temperature. Most enzymes cannot tolerate temperatures higher than 45°C.

Usually enzymes are **specific**. This means that they will only catalyse one kind of reaction. Most enzymes work on one particular molecule, however some digestive enzymes are able to act on a range of closely related molecules. Lipase for example will break down a number of types of fat during digestion.

The effect of temperature on enzyme activity

Iodine turns from brown to blue/black when it is added to starch (see page 35).

If some amylase (the enzyme in saliva) is added to a mixture of iodine and starch solution this blue/black colour will slowly disappear. This is because the amylase has hydrolysed (broken down) the starch into sugar.

By noting the time taken for the blue/black colour to disappear we are able to work out how fast the amylase breaks down the starch. This is called the rate of reaction.

When this experiment is repeated at different temperature the rate of the reaction changes. The graph shows you this change.

We can easily see the effect of heat on the protein in an egg.

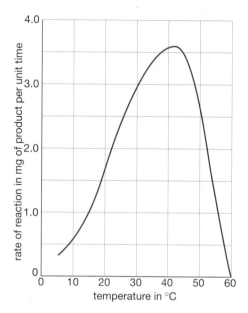

Graph showing the effect of temperature on enzyme activity

Questions

(Questions 1 and 2 refer to the graph.)

1 **a)** What is the rate of reaction
at   i) 10°C   ii) 20°C   iii) 30°C?
b) What happens to the rate of reaction every 10°C?

2 **a)** What is the temperature that gives the highest rate of reaction?
b) What happens to the rate of reaction above this temperature?
c) What do you suppose happens to the enzyme at around 60°C? (*Hint*: remember the egg!)

3 Amylase is one of the enzymes in your body. Your normal body temperature is about 37°C. When you get a disease your body temperature usually rises. Why do you suppose doctors take your temperature regularly when you get a bad infection of a disease?

4 **a)** Give two ways in which a mammal like an elephant can stop its body temperature from getting too high.
b) Why do you suppose 'cold blooded' animals like lizards need to warm themselves up by sunbathing before they can move quickly?

Food tests

You can find out what foods contain by carrying out a few simple chemical tests in the laboratory.

Testing food for starch
Add a few drops of iodine on to the food sample. If any starch is present in the food it will change the colour of the iodine from brown to blue-black.

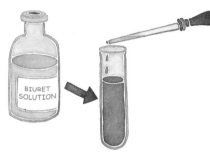

Testing food for protein
Mix the sample with about 3 cm³ of water in a test tube. (Remember to wear safety glasses.) Shake the mixture, then add a few drops of Biuret solution. If protein is present, the colour of the solution will change to purple.

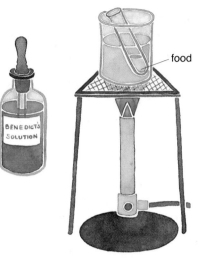

Testing food for glucose
Mix the food sample with some water in a test tube and add a few drops of Benedict's solution. Put the test tube in a water bath and heat carefully. (Remember to wear safety glasses.) If glucose is present the colour of the solution will change from blue to green to brick red depending upon the amount of glucose.

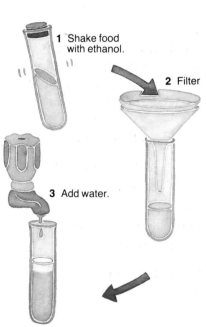

1 Shake food with ethanol.

2 Filter

3 Add water.

Testing food for fat
Thoroughly shake the food sample with some ethanol in a test tube. Filter the mixture into a clean test tube and then add some clean water to the filtrate (the clear liquid which comes through the filter). The presence of fat in the food will be indicated by a white, cloudy emulsion.

Questions

1 Describe how you would find out if
   a) milk contains protein
   b) cheese contains fat
   c) biscuits contain glucose
   d) potato contains starch.

2 What safety precautions should you take when carrying out food tests?

3 Find out what an emulsion is.

4 Find out what 'Clinistix' and 'Albustix' are used for. (Try your local chemist's shop!)

Absorbing digested food

The food which has been broken down during digestion has to be **absorbed** into the blood system before the body can use it.

The digested food particles are so small that they can pass through the wall of the gut (the intestine) by **diffusion**. Diffusion in liquids is a slow process. To make sure that enough food passes into the blood the intestine has a special structure:

- It is long and therefore has a large surface area for absorbing food.

- Its walls are covered with thousands of tiny projections called **villi**. This increases the surface area still further.

- Its lining is very thin, usually only one cell thick, which allows the easy passage of digested food across it and into the blood.

- It is well supplied with blood vessels to carry away food.

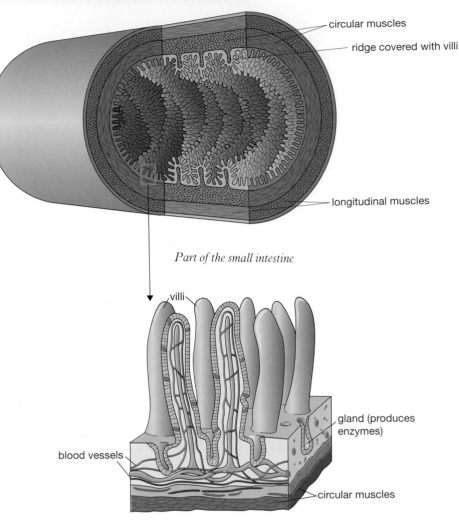

Part of the small intestine

Wall of the small intestine

Food is carried in the blood to the liver. The liver processes food before releasing it to the body for use.

Some material in the food we eat cannot be digested. It consists mainly of cellulose in plant cell walls and is called **roughage**. Roughage is passed into the large intestine where water is absorbed from it before it is expelled through the anus in faeces. This final stage is called **egestion**.

Questions

1 Give *four* ways that the intestine is adapted to absorb digested food.

2 Why are these adaptations needed?

3 What happens to food after the gut absorbs it?

4 What is roughage?

5 Find out more about the liver. What jobs does it do? Why are these important to the body?

Foods containing roughage

The kidneys and excretion

Our bodies contain a large amount of water. Much of it is in our blood. We get our water from food and from the liquids we drink. We lose water from our bodies as we breathe out, when we sweat, and when we urinate. The balance of water and salts in the body must be carefully controlled if we are to stay healthy.

The sensor for the water control system is a part of the brain containing the hypothalamus and a small structure called the **pituitary gland**. As blood flows through the hypothalamus, the amount of water is monitored. If the water level is too low, the hypothalamus makes the pituitary gland release a chemical known as **ADH** (anti-diuretic hormone) into the blood. This acts as a message to the **kidneys**, where the water level is controlled.

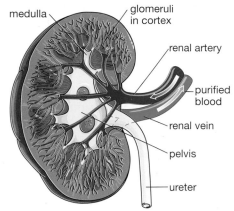
Section through a kidney

We have two kidneys. One of their functions is to control the amount of water in our blood. The outer part of the kidney is called the **cortex**. This part contains very small 'knots' of thin blood capillaries. Each 'knot' is called a **glomerulus**. The inner part of the kidney is called the **medulla**. This part contains about a million tiny tubes called **nephrons**.

Each nephron starts in a cup-shaped structure called the **Bowman's capsule**. A glomerulus sits in this cup, as shown in the diagram. As blood flows through the capillaries, substances such as water and dissolved salts are filtered when they pass into the Bowman's capsule. Large molecules such as proteins cannot pass through the wall of the capillary and so are left in the blood.

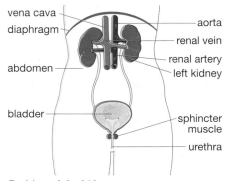
Position of the kidneys

The liquid that does pass into the Bowman's capsule is mainly water and waste materials. Any useful substances which have got through, such as glucose, are reabsorbed by blood vessels. The rest of the liquid passes down the long, looped part of the nephron called the **loop of Henle**. If more water is needed in the body, a lot of it is reabsorbed here by the capillaries of the kidney's main vein, the **renal vein**.

After the necessary water has been reabsorbed, the nephron holds a solution containing waste materials such as **urea**. The solution is called **urine**. This passes through a tube called the **ureter** to the **bladder**. Urine is stored in the bladder until it is passed out of the body. **Blood leaving the kidney is purified and contains the correct amount of water.** Urine leaving the body carries away unwanted water and any unwanted substances.

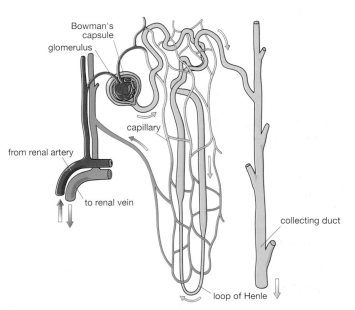
Enlarged view showing a nephron

Questions

1 Where is the water content of the blood 'detected'?

2 How are messages sent from brain to kidneys?

3 What is a capillary? What is a glomerulus?

4 Why can't protein molecules pass from the glomerulus into the Bowman's capsule?

5 If the blood water level is too low, where do the blood vessels reabsorb water from the nephron? What else is reabsorbed here?

6 Why do we say that the body's water control system uses negative feedback?

The air is a mixture of gases, one of which is **oxygen**. Oxygen is needed by all living things so that energy can be released from food during respiration.

During breathing, air is taken into two lungs, oxgyen is removed and carried in the blood to body cells. Carbon dioxide and water, produced in the cells during respiration, leave the body by the reverse process.

Breathing in

The muscles between the ribs contract lifting the rib cage up and out, expanding the chest. At the same time muscles contract to flatten the **diaphragm**. This makes the space inside the rib cage bigger and reduces the air pressure in the lungs. Air moves into the lungs from outside because there the air pressure is higher.

Breathing out

The rib and diaphragm muscles relax. This lowers the chest and raises the diaphragm. The space in the rib cage gets smaller so the air pressure increases. This forces air out of the lungs.

The table shows the amount of different gases in the air we breathe in (**inhaled**) and the air we breathe out (**exhaled**).

gas	inhaled	exhaled
nitrogen	78%	78%
oxygen	21%	17%
carbon dioxide	0.03%	4%
water vapour	varies	saturated

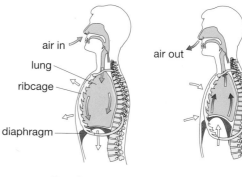

Breathing in   *Breathing out*

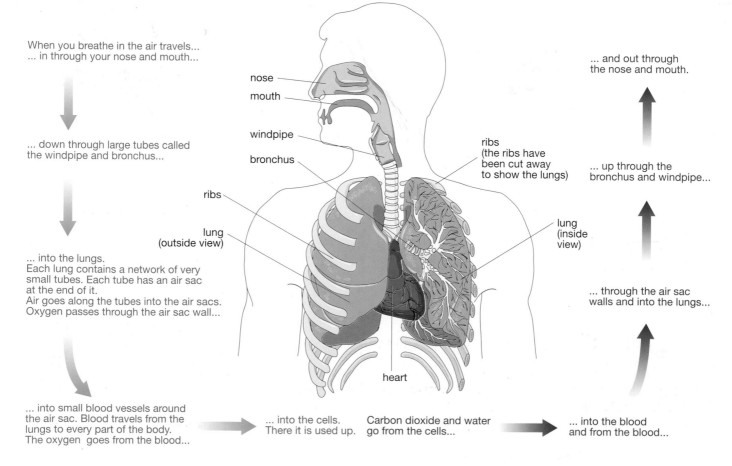

When you breathe in the air travels...
... in through your nose and mouth...

... down through large tubes called the windpipe and bronchus...

... into the lungs.
Each lung contains a network of very small tubes. Each tube has an air sac at the end of it.
Air goes along the tubes into the air sacs.
Oxygen passes through the air sac wall...

... into small blood vessels around the air sac. Blood travels from the lungs to every part of the body.
The oxygen goes from the blood...

... into the cells.
There it is used up.

Carbon dioxide and water go from the cells...

... into the blood and from the blood...

... through the air sac walls and into the lungs...

... up through the bronchus and windpipe...

... and out through the nose and mouth.

nose
mouth
windpipe
bronchus
ribs
lung
(outside view)

ribs
(the ribs have been cut away to show the lungs)

lung
(inside view)

heart

Lungs in more detail

The lungs are two elastic pouches lying inside the ribs. They are connected to the air outside the body by the windpipe or **trachea**. This opens into the back of the mouth and nose. The trachea divides into two smaller tubes called **bronchi**. One of these goes into each lung before dividing further into smaller tubes called **bronchioles**. After yet more branching the tubes end in tiny, thin walled air sacs called **alveoli**.

Lining all of the air passages are two types of cells. One type is covered with tiny hairs called **cilia**. The other produces a sticky liquid called **mucus**. Small dust particles and bacteria stick to the mucus. The cilia 'beat' to carry the mucus up to the back of the mouth where it is swallowed.

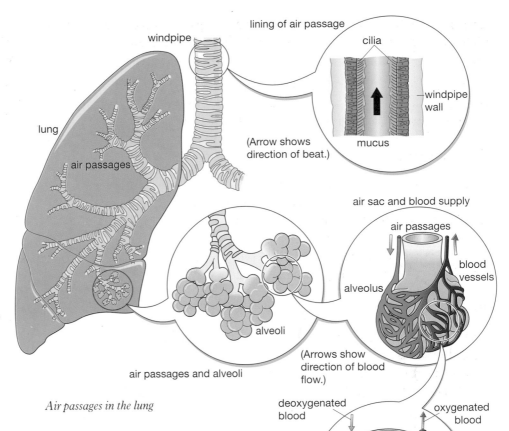

Air passages in the lung

A single alveolus

Oxygen moves into the blood system by diffusion. The alveoli are well adapted to speed up this process.

- Because there are thousands of very small alveoli, there is a very big surface area for the oxygen to diffuse across.
- The walls of the alveoli are very thin – in places just one cell thick.
- The lining of the alveoli is moist so that the oxygen can dissolve.
- The alveoli are surrounded by a dense network of tiny blood vessels called capillaries. These carry the oxygen away.

Activities

Comparing inhaled and exhaled air
The diagram alongside shows a simple piece of apparatus that you can make in school. Tube *M* is placed in your mouth and then you breathe slowly and gently in and out. The air entering your lungs has to pass through the calcium hydroxide solution (lime water) in test tube *A*. Air leaving your lungs has to bubble through the calcium hydroxide solution in test tube *B*.

As you breathe, the solution in test tube *B* turns a milky white colour. Find out what this shows.

After some time, the solution in test tube *A* turns a faint white colour. What does this show?

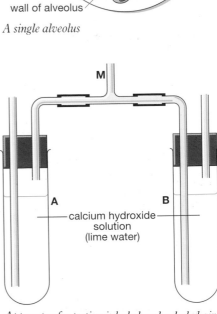

Apparatus for testing inhaled and exhaled air

Breathing can be dangerous

The air around us is not always as clean as we would like it to be. Not everyone can live high up on mountain sides where the air is fresh and clean. Most of us breathe polluted air which may contain dangerous substances that can damage our health. There are times when it is impossible to avoid breathing in dirty air but some people deliberately breathe in harmful substances! Glue sniffing and smoking are two activities that can seriously damage health.

Glue sniffing

Glue sniffers breathe the vapours given off from certain types of glue and other products in order to get 'high'. The most common products used are the solvents in glue and adhesives, lighter fuel, paint thinners and dry-cleaning agents. These cause mental confusion and hallucinations. They can also cause serious damage to the lungs and brain. Some glue sniffers have died by suffocating on their vomit ('sick') while under the influence of the solvent. Others have suffocated in plastic bags placed over the head whilst sniffing. Most glue sniffers are young people of school age. Attempts have been made to stop shopkeepers from selling glues and solvents to young people.

Smoking

Smoking kills about 50 000 people every year in Britain.

Tobacco smoke contains many chemicals which are harmful to the body.

Nicotine is an addictive drug which is absorbed into the bloodstream and seems to affect the heart, blood vessels and nervous system. It raises blood pressure, which may lead to coronary heart disease (CHD). Nicotine also affects the cilia lining the air passages in the lungs. The natural protection against dust and bacteria is lost and frequent coughing is necessary in order to keep the passages clear. Bacteria infect the air passages making them narrower. This can lead to the difficult and painful breathing associated with **bronchitis** and **emphysema**. Both conditions lead to a reduction of the surface area available for gas exchange and so the sufferers get very 'short of breath'.

Carbon monoxide from cigarette smoke gets into the blood and combines with haemoglobin in the red cells. Oxygen transport around the body is seriously affected. When tobacco smoke cools it forms **tar** which sticks to the lining of the lungs and collects in the alveoli. It is the chemicals in this tar which irritate the lungs and may cause lung cancer.

Smokers affect other people too

Many people who do not smoke find it unpleasant to be in a smoke-filled room. The smoke in the air contains higher concentrations of poisonous chemicals, twice as much nicotine, three times more tar, five times more carbon monoxide. No wonder non-smokers suffer from sore eyes, coughs and headaches. Their clothing smells of cigarette smoke too!

Do you want a cigarette more than you want your baby?

When a pregnant woman smokes she puts her unborn baby's life at risk. Every time she inhales, she poisons her baby's bloodstream with nicotine and carbon monoxide.
Smoking can restrict your baby's growth inside the womb. It can make him underdeveloped and underweight at birth.
It can even kill him.
In just one year, in Britain alone, over 1,000 babies might not have died if their mothers had given up smoking when they were pregnant.
If you give up smoking when you're pregnant your baby will be as healthy as if you'd never smoked.   The Health Education Council
Helping you to better health

Questions

1 What does the graph show you?

2 What is the death rate from lung cancer for those who smoke 30 cigarettes a day?

3 Explain why smoking can damage your health.

4 Why do you think people take up smoking or glue sniffing?

5 Suggest how young people could be educated so that they do not take up smoking.

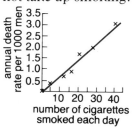

Graph showing the death rate from lung cancer among men who smoke

Getting it around the body (1): blood

What is blood?

Blood consists of a watery, straw coloured liquid called **plasma**. **Red cells**, **white cells** and **platelets** are carried in the plasma. Since there are many more red cells than white cells our blood always looks red. The body of an adult human contains about 5 litres of blood.

Clot formation
Platelets are tiny pieces of cells broken off larger cells in the bone marrow. They play an important part in the clotting of blood. At a cut platelets form a plug preventing continuous bleeding. Gradually a pad of fibres forms beneath the plug and red cells become trapped in it – this is a clot. The surface of a clot hardens off to form a scab.

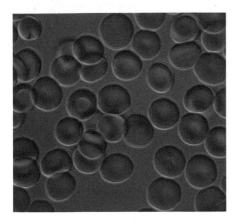

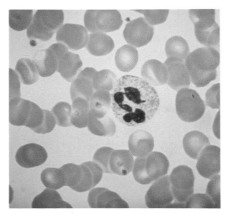

Red blood cells
Red cells transport oxygen from the lungs. They are made in bone marrow and contain a chemical called haemoglobin which makes them red. Oxygen combines with **haemoglobin** *at the lungs to make oxyhaemoglobin. As it travels round the body oxyhaemoglobin slowly releases its oxygen to the cells and changes back to haemoglobin.*

$$Oxygen + Haemoglobin \underset{cells}{\overset{lungs}{\rightleftharpoons}} Oxyhaemoglobin$$

White blood cells
White cells are part of the body's defensive system. Many engulf and destroy any microbes that get into your body through cuts or via your lungs or digestive system. Other white cells produce **antibodies** *which change the poisonous chemicals produced by microbes into harmless substances.*

Blood after spinning in a centrifuge
If blood is spun in a centrifuge the cells and platelets will sink to the bottom of the glass tube leaving the straw-coloured plasma at the top.

Plasma is water in which food, waste material and other substances are dissolved.

What does blood do?

Blood carries chemicals and other substances around the body, that is why the blood and vessels in which it flows is called a **transport system**.

- It carries oxygen from the lungs and food from the digestive system to the cells of the body where it is needed for energy production.
- It carries carbon dioxide from the cells to the lungs where it is removed and breathed out of the body.
- It carries waste materials from body tissues to the kidneys where they are excreted.
- It prevents infection by healing wounds and destroying invading microbes. (You can read more about the prevention of infection on page 57.)

Questions

1 How much blood is there in the body of an adult human being?

2 Why have we got a blood system?

3 What is plasma and what does it do?

4 What differences are there in the shape, structure and function of red and white blood cells?

5 What does haemoglobin do in the body?

The heart is a muscular pump. It pushes blood around the body through tubes called blood vessels.

Blood vessels

Arteries carry blood away from the heart. They have thick muscular walls to withstand the high pressure and usually lie deep inside the body. Arteries divide into small **capillaries** which penetrate into all body tissues so that the blood supply is close to every cell in the body. The transfer of gases, food and excretory products between blood and cells takes place by diffusion through the thin capillary walls. Capillaries join up to form **veins** which return the blood to the heart. Pressure in veins is usually low and valves are present to make sure that blood flows only in one direction.

The heart

The heart is a pump made of muscle. It is probably the best pump ever made since it never stops working from well before you are born until you die. The space inside is divided into four chambers. The top two are the **atria** and the bottom two, the **ventricles**.

Blood from the body enters the right atrium through a large blood vessel called the **vena cava**. Blood from the lungs enters the left atrium through the **pulmonary vein**. The atria contract together pushing blood down into the ventricles. From the left ventricle blood is pumped to the body through the aorta and from the right ventricle to the lungs along the pulmonary artery. Both ventricles contract at the same time.

Every contraction of the atria and ventricles is called a heartbeat. In fact there is really a double beat since the atria contract just before the ventricles. This is important if blood is to flow in the right direction through the heart. There are valves between the upper and lower chambers which prevent any possible backflow of blood.

Your heart beats about 70 times a minute when you are resting but this increases to well over 100 times a minute during physical activity or excitement. You can easily measure your heartbeat by finding your **pulse**. This is a surge of blood produced in the arteries every time the ventricles contract. A pulse can be felt with the finger tips at the wrist where an artery passes over bone close to the surface of the skin.

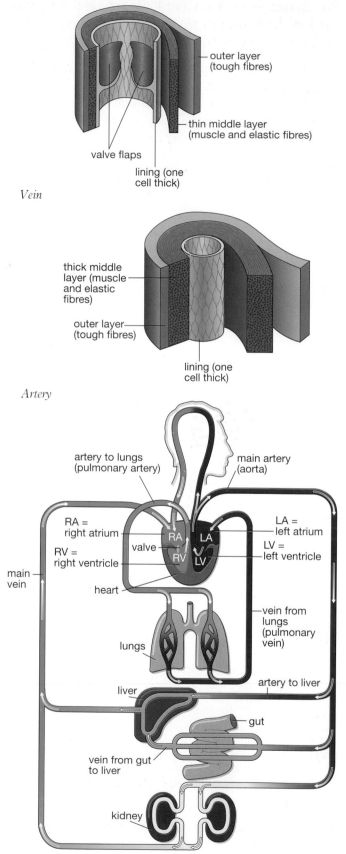

Vein

Artery

The human circulatory system

Exchange at tissues

Blood, carrying oxygen and food, travels through the arteries to all parts of the body. You will have read on page 41 that oxygen is carried in the red blood cells. Food is dissolved in the plasma.

When blood reaches body cells, oxygen and food leave in a solution called tissue fluid before entering the cells by diffusion. **Tissue fluid** is mainly water. It forms a continuous link between the water in the blood and the water in the body cells. This is the reason why fresh meat always looks and feels wet.

Waste substances such as carbon dioxide and urea travel in the opposite direction. They pass into the tissue fluid, then into the blood in the capillaries.

Capillaries join together to form veins. The pulmonary vein carries blood to the lungs where the carbon dioxide is **excreted**. The renal vein takes blood to the kidneys, where excretion of urea takes place.

(You can read more about excretion in the kidneys and the lungs on pages 37 and 38.)

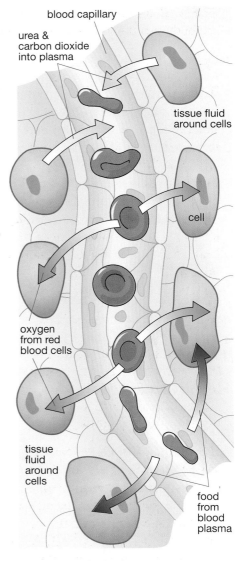

The process of diffusion

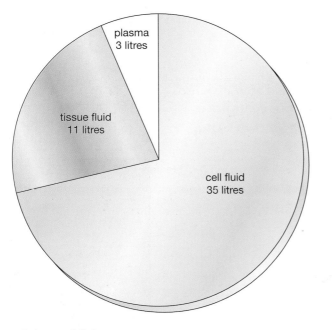

Where the water is in an adult human.

Questions

1 What carries **a**) food and **b**) oxygen to the body cells?

2 By what process do food and oxygen enter our body cells?

3 **a**) Name *two* waste substances produced in body cells.
   b) Where are these substances excreted?

4 Name the *large* blood vessels that carry waste to the excretory organs.

5 **a**) How much water is there in the body of an adult human?
   b) Where is most of this water found?

Coronary heart disease

Coronary heart disease (CHD) kills more people in Britain than any other illness.

The heart like all other muscles in the body requires a good supply of food and oxygen. It gets this through its own blood supply carried in the **coronary arteries**. The coronary arteries are very narrow and as a person gets older, these arteries become 'furred up' with fatty deposits (cholesterol). The arteries become narrower and the blood supply to the heart is reduced. This means that when the heart has to work harder oxygen cannot get to the heart muscle fast enough and a cramp-like pain spreads across the chest. This pain is called **angina** and usually fades after a few minutes rest. Drugs can help relieve the pain, they cause the arteries to widen and allow more blood through.

A heart attack is caused when a coronary artery becomes completely blocked, usually by a blood clot getting jammed in an artery already narrowed by cholesterol. This is called a **coronary thrombosis** ('coronary'). With its blood supply cut off, part of the heart muscle will die causing severe pain or even cardiac arrest where the heart stops beating altogether. Unless the heart can be started again quickly, the person will die.

How to avoid CHD

Medical research has shown that coronary heart disease tends to run in families, it affects older people more than younger ones and men are more likely to suffer from it than women. Obviously you have no control over your family history, age or sex but there are some things you can do to greatly reduce the chances of suffering from heart disease:

- don't smoke at all – it raises the blood pressure
- don't drink too much alcohol – it also raises blood pressure
- eat the right kinds of food – fat (cholesterol) 'furs up' arteries
- exercise regularly to strengthen the heart
- relax more and try to avoid stressful situations.

People who have heart attacks have often ignored these 'rules'.

Blood transfusions

Sometimes people need to be given the blood of another person. This is called a **blood transfusion**. Blood transfusions are sometimes necessary during long operations or to help in the treatment of diseases such as leukaemia (blood cancer). Hospitals in England and Wales need about 5000 litres of blood every day of the year. As medical techniques become more advanced the demand will rise even further.

The *National Blood Transfusion Service* organises the collection of blood from blood donors. Blood donors are very special people, they could give the vital gift of life to someone else.

Treatment for CHD

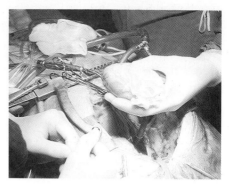

A diseased heart may be replaced completely with a healthy organ taken from another person.

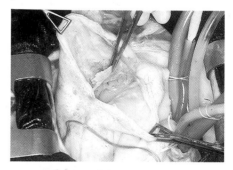

Over 5000 people each year have **heart bypass surgery**. *A piece of vein is removed from elsewhere in the body and used to bypass the blocked coronary artery.*

An artificial pacemaker can be implanted if a heart attack destroys the heart's pacemaker (muscle).

Reproduction (1): males and females

The time when boys and girls become sexually mature is called **puberty**. Puberty usually starts at the age of 11–13 in girls and about 12–14 in boys. People vary a great deal and so there is nothing wrong with you if puberty comes earlier or later in your life.

What happens at puberty?

As well as growing fast (perhaps 15 cm or more in a year), at puberty we develop secondary sexual characteristics. In women these include breasts and a more rounded figure. Men grow more facial hair and develop a more muscular body and a deeper voice. Hair grows under the arms of both sexes and around a woman's vagina and a man's penis.

Puberty is the time when reproductive organs start to produce **gametes**. These are the sex cells which are involved in reproduction.

At puberty, girls start to produce mature eggs in their ovaries. They will notice this because each month they will lose a small amount of blood through the vagina. This is known as **menstruation** (see page 48).

Boys start to produce sperms in their testes. Occasionally these sperms will be ejected with seminal fluid during the night. These 'wet dreams' are completely natural and quite harmless.

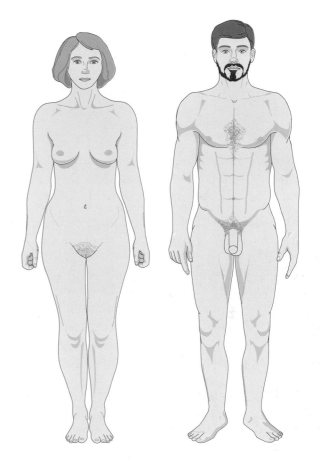

Male and female bodies

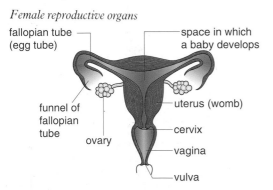

Female reproductive organs

fallopian tube (egg tube)
space in which a baby develops
funnel of fallopian tube
uterus (womb)
ovary
cervix
vagina
vulva

The ovaries contain thousands of potential egg cells when a girl is born. However, only a very small number will ever mature later in life.

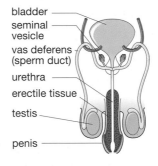

Male reproductive organs

bladder
seminal vesicle
vas deferens (sperm duct)
urethra
erectile tissue
testis
penis

The lining of the tubes which make up the testes consists of cells which are constantly making sperms. Billions of sperms will be made during a lifetime.

Questions

1 Where are male sex cells made?

2 What are female sex cells called?

3 Explain why a boy does not need to shave until he reaches his mid-teens.

4 Describe the changes that take place in the body of **a)** a boy **b)** a girl during puberty.

5 Girls can sing high notes all through their life but boys are unable to do so after the age of about 14. Why is this?

Reproduction (2): fertilization

An egg is fertilized when the nucleus of a single sperm fuses with the egg nucleus.

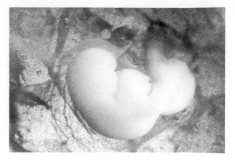

... at 2 weeks eyes develop, arms and legs are just bumps.

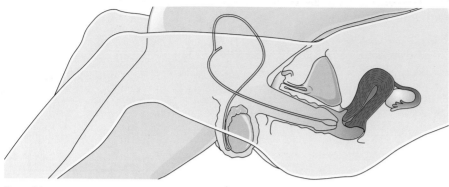

Sexual intercourse

For sperm to meet an egg, **mating** or **sexual intercourse** must take place. During sexual excitement the man's penis becomes enlarged and stiff (erect) due to an increase in blood supply. This erection makes it possible for the penis to be pushed into a woman's vagina. The sensitive tip of the penis is stimulated by being moved up and down the vagina. After a while, muscular contractions of the sperm tubes ejaculate sperm into the vagina. The good sensation felt by the man during ejaculation is called an orgasm. A woman may also experience an orgasm during sexual intercourse. About 400 million sperm are released by the man during each ejaculation. The sperm are mixed with seminal fluid. Seminal fluid contains chemicals that nourish the sperm and encourage them to start swimming. Sperm travel through the womb and up the oviducts, where an egg may be waiting. If the egg is fertilized it divides repeatedly to form a ball of cells which passes down the oviduct and attaches itself to the prepared wall of the womb. The fertilized egg is called a **zygote**.

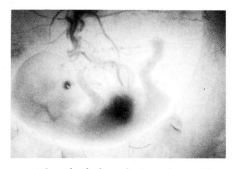

... at 6 weeks the heart begins to beat and hands and feet begin to grow.

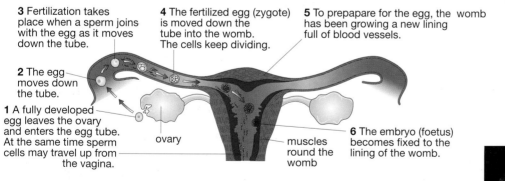

3 Fertilization takes place when a sperm joins with the egg as it moves down the tube.

4 The fertilized egg (zygote) is moved down the tube into the womb. The cells keep dividing.

5 To prepapare for the egg, the womb has been growing a new lining full of blood vessels.

2 The egg moves down the tube.

1 A fully developed egg leaves the ovary and enters the egg tube. At the same time sperm cells may travel up from the vagina.

ovary

muscles round the womb

6 The embryo (foetus) becomes fixed to the lining of the womb.

Fertilization of an egg

The cells in the ball divide over and over again to produce tissues and organs. During the next 9 months the developing baby, or **embryo** grows inside its mother. This is called the **gestation period** or **pregnancy**.

Pregnancy usually lasts for about 38 weeks. After this period of time the baby is ready to be born.

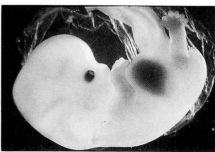

... at 12 weeks the baby begins to move its arms and legs. Fingers and toes are formed.

Reproduction (3): birth

During pregnancy the womb will have become thickened with extra cells and supplied with an increased blood supply. Connecting the embryo to the womb wall is the **umbilical cord** and **placenta**. These are formed from the tissues of the embryo as it develops. A bag, the **amnion**, filled with a liquid called amniotic fluid surrounds and protects the embryo throughout pregnancy.

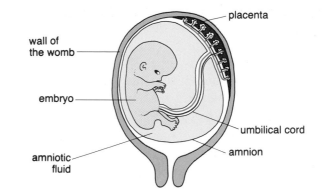

An embryo in the womb

The placenta extends into the womb wall and substances dissolved in the mother's blood pass across it into the baby's blood system. It controls the entry of materials into the baby's blood, keeping out many harmful substances and allowing essential ones like food and oxygen in. Unfortunately alcohol, nicotine and some drugs can pass through this barrier. This is why a pregnant woman should avoid drinking alcohol and smoking cigarettes. She should also take drugs only when they have been prescribed by a doctor. Waste passes from the baby's blood to the mother's.

The blood system of mother and baby never actually mix. The mother's blood pressure would damage the developing circulatory system of the baby and if the blood groups were different it could cause clotting.

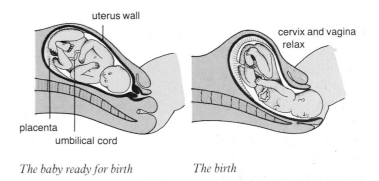

The baby ready for birth   *The birth*

A few weeks before birth the baby usually turns upside-down so that its head is just above the neck of the womb. 'Labour pains' start when the womb begins to contract rhythmically – slowly at first, then quicker and stronger. Muscular contractions of the womb break the amnion and fluid is released. The neck of the womb relaxes and baby's head passes through. Eventually contractions of the womb together with those of the abdomen muscles, push the baby through the vagina and out into the world.

During the first months of its life outside the womb the baby will get all the food it needs from its mother. It suckles milk produced in the **mammary glands** inside its mother's breasts. As it gets older the growing child will begin to eat solid food.

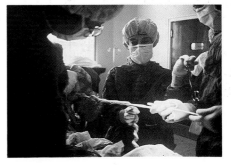

The birth of a baby

Questions

1 What is meant by the following words
 a) erection **b)** ejaculation **c)** fertilization?
2 What happens to the penis before sexual intercourse?
3 Describe what happens to a sperm from ejaculation to fertilization.
4 Describe what happens to an egg after fertilization.
5 What is the placenta for?
6 What are 'labour pains'?
7 Try to find out how long pregnancy lasts in **a)** a mouse
 b) a dog **c)** a human **d)** an elephant. What pattern can you see?

Factors affecting human birth weight

The weight of a baby when it is born depends very much upon what the mother eats during pregnancy. A diet containing plenty of protein and vitamins helps the embryo develop into a normal healthy baby.

Pregnant women who smoke frequently have premature (early) births. They also produce babies that are smaller.

Reproduction (4): menstruation

Many hundreds of eggs are produced by a sexually mature woman. These are released approximately one per month. It is very unlikely however that more than a very small number of these eggs will ever be fertilized either because sexual intercourse hasn't taken place or it took place at a time when an egg wasn't present in an oviduct.

Eggs only live for a short time, about 48 hours. When an egg is not fertilized the thickened lining of the womb disintegrates. Unwanted cells together with some blood are pushed from the womb. The waste material is moved out of the body through the vagina by contractions of the womb wall. This monthly loss of blood is called menstruation or a **period**. A period lasts for about five days and can cause some discomfort. This is because the contractions of the womb wall can cause cramp-like pains. These pains can usually be treated with pain-killing tablets like paracetamol.

To absorb the blood lost during menstruation women wear sanitary towels or tampons which must be changed regularly.

Many women get depressed and irritable during the days before menstruation. This is often referred to as **pre-menstrual tension** or PMT.

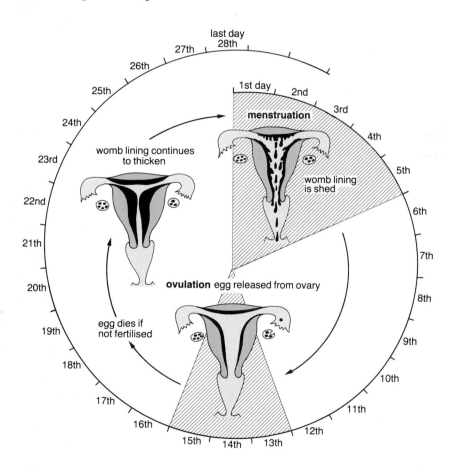

The menstrual cycle

Questions

1   If a woman begins to produce eggs at the age of 13 and stops at 48, roughly how many eggs will she produce during her life?

2   During one menstrual cycle a woman's period started on March 16th. On what date would an egg be released from an ovary? (The diagram will help you.)

3   What changes take place in the wall of the womb as it prepares to receive a fertilized egg?

4   What changes take place in the wall of the womb if it does not receive a fertilized egg?

5   What is the purpose of menstruation?

6   Why do you think menstruation stops when a woman is pregnant?

Contraceptives and STDs: things you should know about

Sexual intercourse is pleasurable and is a natural extension of the love between a man and a woman. However, if the couple do not want to have a child they must somehow stop a sperm from fertilizing an egg. Fertilization can be prevented by the use of contraceptives. There is a number of types:

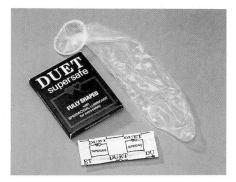
Condom

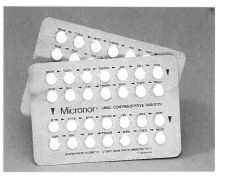
Contraceptive pills

Coil

What are STDs?

STDs are **sexually transmitted diseases**. These are passed on during sexual activity. They affect the reproductive organs mainly but can spread to other body parts. Some of the more common STDs include Gonorrhoea, Syphilis, Genital Herpes, NSU (Non Specific Urethritis), TV (Trichomoniasis Vaginalis), Thrush (Candidiasis) and lice or 'crabs'.

The microbes causing an STD cannot live for long outside the body therefore it is very unlikely that they can be caught by anything other than sexual intercourse.

AIDS

AIDS (Acquired Immune Deficiency Syndrome) is a disease which damages the body's natural defensive system. People with AIDS are unable to fight off infections that the body would normally resist. Such infections are usually fatal.

AIDS is not easy to catch. The microbe causing it, a virus, cannot live outside the body so AIDS cannot be spread by coughing, sneezing or drinking from the same cup. The virus is passed from one person to another when blood, semen or vaginal fluids are mixed. This may happen during sexual intercourse or when injecting drugs with used needles or syringes.

There is as yet no known cure for AIDS. So it is important to follow some simple rules if you are to reduce the risk of infection.

- Have few sexual partners. Unless you are sure of your partner always use a condom.
- People who use drugs should never share syringes, needles etc.
- If you have your ears pierced or body tattooed always make sure that equipment is sterilized first.

The Condom
The condom is a thin rubber sheath that is fitted over the erect penis before intercourse. Ejaculated sperm is collected in a small bulb at the tip. Though not perfect as contraceptives, condoms have no physical side effects and are the only method of birth control that help prevent STDs.

The Pill
The pill contains a delicate balance of hormones that prevent ovulation. The pill is prescribed by a doctor and must be taken exactly as instructed. Though regarded as a reliable contraceptive, there are possible side effects such as weight gain.

The Coil
The intra uterine device (IUD) is a small coil or loop of plastic inserted by a doctor into the womb. Its presence in the womb appears to prevent implantation of the fertilised egg. IUDs are not 100% effective and sometimes there are side effects such as very heavy periods.

Sight

Sight is perhaps our most useful sense. Try closing your eyes for a few minutes and think of the problems faced by those who are blind.

Eyes are the sense organs of sight. Our eyes are in sockets in the skull. This helps to protect them from damage. The eyes are held in place by muscles. These let us move our eyes from side to side and up and down.

We have two eyes a few centimetres apart. This helps us judge distances and find the position of things easily. The image from each eye is slightly different. The brain puts the two images together to give a 3-D (three-dimensional) effect. This is called **stereoscopic vision**.

How do the eyes work?

Light from an object enters the eye. It is focused by the **cornea** and the **lens** to give a sharp image on the **retina**. The image is small and upside down. The shape of the lens can be changed by a ring of muscle running around its edge. As the ring of muscle contracts or relaxes the lens changes shape. This lets us focus on objects at different distances.

A healthy lens is clear to allow light to pass through easily. Sometimes however it may become cloudy or opaque causing blurred vision or total blindness. This condition is known as a **cataract**. Cataracts are usually associated with old age. Cataracts can be removed surgically. Usually the complete lens is removed and replaced with a plastic lens.

On the retina are millions of light-sensitive cells. Each one is linked to the brain by several nerve fibres. The brain interprets signals from the retina and produces the 'picture' that you see.

There are two kinds of light-sensitive cells – **rods** which are sensitive to light intensity and **cones** which recognise colours.

Rod cells tend to be located around the edge of the retina. Cone cells are found only in the central part of the retina, the **fovea**, and work best in bright light. Have you ever noticed that you cannot see the colour of objects in a dimly lit room?

The amount of light entering the eye is controlled by the **iris**. The muscles of the iris change the size of the **pupil** to allow more or less light to pass through.

Questions

1 Explain why it is an advantage for rabbits to have two eyes, one on each side of the head.

2 What happens to the iris and the pupil when a person in a dark room turns on a bright light?

3 What do the ciliary muscles do to the shape of the lens?

4 Why can't you see coloured objects in a darkened room?

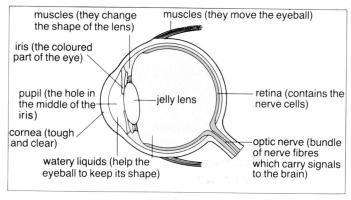

The eye

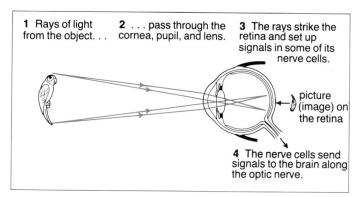

This is what happens when you look at an object.

Activities

1 Hold a pencil at arm's length so that it points upwards. Look at the pencil using one eye. Now, without moving the pencil, look at it using the other eye. You will see that the pencil seems to change position.

2 Hold a pencil in each hand, at arm's length so that they point towards one another. Close one eye and then move the pencils closer together to make their points touch. Repeat the experiment with both eyes open. Which is easier?

Hearing and balance

Hearing

We have one ear on each side of the head. This helps us to tell where a sound is coming from. Ears change vibrations in the air into nerve impulses which travel to the brain where they are interpreted as sound. These vibrations or sound waves are collected by the funnel-like **pinna** and passed down a short canal to the **eardrum**. The eardrum is a thin, tightly stretched membrane which vibrates in time with vibrations in the air.

There is a small air-filled space behind the eardrum connected to the back of the mouth by the **eustachian tube**. This helps to keep the air pressure the same on both sides of the eardrum. Sometimes pressure changes occur outside the ear such as when you take off or land in an aeroplane. This can cause pain. The pressure inside the ear can be equalized by making air enter or leave through the eustachian tube by swallowing or yawning.

Three tiny bones, the hammer, anvil and stirrup, link the eardrum to the oval window. These bones transmit and amplify the vibrations of the eardrum, increasing their force by over 20 times. As a result the oval window is moved in and out sending more vibrations through fluid in a coiled tube called the **cochlea**. Nerve endings in the cochlea detect vibrations in the fluid and signals are sent along a nerve to the brain.

Balance

Your eyes will usually tell you if you are standing upright or not. However, a lot of information about balance comes from structures in the ear called the **sacculus** and **semi-circular canals**.

The sacculus is filled with liquid and lined with sensory hair cells. The hairs of these cells are attached to small, chalk granules. When the head is tilted the chalk pulls on the hairs. The hairs then send signals to the brain where they are translated into information about the movement.

Semi-circular canals are three curved tubes, also filled with fluid, arranged at right angles to each other. Each

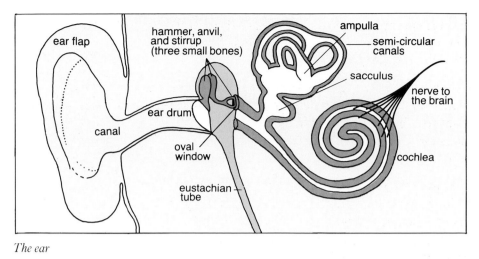

The ear

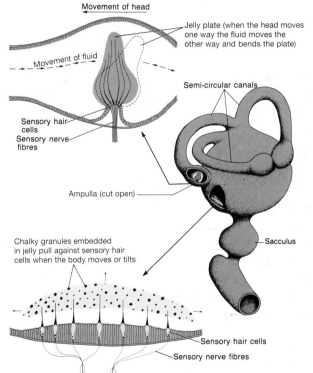

Section through an ampulla

canal has a swelling at the end called the **ampulla**. The ampullae contain structures like those found in the sacculus except that a jelly plate replaces the chalky granules. When the liquid in the canals moves, the jelly plates are pushed to one side and nerve impulses are sent to the brain as before.

The arrangement of semi-circular canals in the head makes it possible for the brain to detect movements in any direction. If you spin around and around then stop suddenly, the liquid in the canals will continue to move against the jelly plates. This confuses the brain and you feel dizzy.

51

Other senses

Spread throughout the skin are **sense receptors** which are sensitive to touch, pressure, temperature. Some give the sensation of pain.

There are many touch and pressure receptors on the fingertips, lips and tongue. They tell you whether surfaces are hard, soft, rough or smooth. Touch receptors are also attached to the root of every hair on your body.

Small temperature changes in the environment can be detected by temperature receptors of which there are two types, hot and cold. The front of the body has more hot receptors than the back, this explains why your back tends to feel cold when you enter a cold room.

The sensation of pain tells you that something is wrong in the body. Free nerve endings detect pain and these are found all over the skin and inside the body.

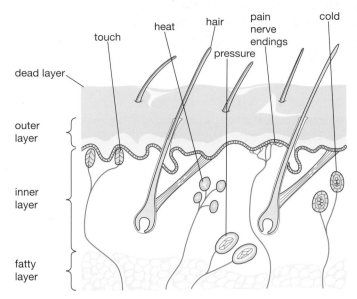

Nerve cells in the skin

Smell receptors in the nose and taste receptors on the tongue both detect chemicals and together are responsible for giving the sensation of flavour in our food.

Olfactory organs at the top of the nose cavity are sensitive to chemicals in the air but only after they have dissolved in the moisture film covering the receptors.

Taste buds are found in between the ridges on the tongue. There are four kinds, each one designed to detect one kind of substance: sweet, salt, sour or bitter. The diagram shows the position of these different taste buds on the tongue.

Taste sensors on the tongue

Activities

1 Collect together the following **a)** salt solution **b)** sugar solution **c)** lemon juice (sour) **d)** cold, strong unsweetened coffee (bitter).

2 Using a clean dropper, carefully place a drop of one of the solutions on one of the areas of your tongue shown in the diagram above.

3 Rinse out your mouth with clean water and repeat the experiment using a different solution and different area of tongue.

4 Carry on doing this until you have tested each area of your tongue with all the solutions.

Are your taste buds arranged on your tongue as they are in the diagram? What advantage is there in moving food around your mouth when you are eating? Why do you appear to lose your sense of taste when you have a cold?

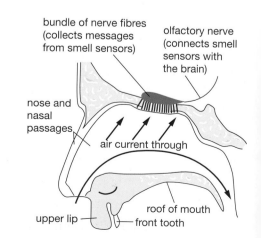

The nose and its smell receptors

Nerves

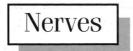

All of our body functions must be **coordinated**. This means that they must be made to work together. Coordination is brought about by the nervous system and the hormone system.

The brain and spinal cord together form the **central nervous system** (CNS). Many nerves branch off from the central nervous system to all parts of the body. Making up the nervous system are special cells called **neurones**. There are two types of neurone – **sensory neurones** which carry messages from sense receptors to the CNS, and **motor neurones** which carry messages from the CNS to the muscles and glands. The messages are carried as tiny electrical impulses.

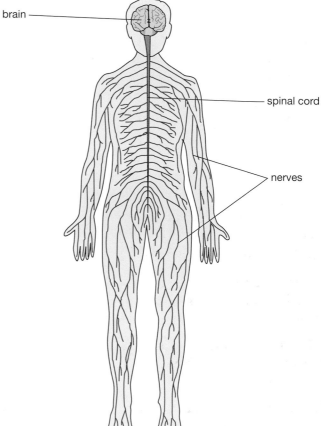

The human nervous system

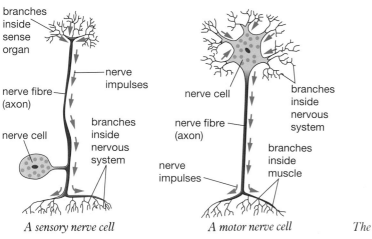

A sensory nerve cell   *A motor nerve cell*

A nerve is a collection of axons from different neurones. It is rather like an electric cable but with an insulation sheath made of myelin rather than plastic.

Nerve impulses pass from one neurone to another by means of a special link called a **synapse**. Branching tips of one neurone lie close to the cell body of another. There is no physical contact between the two. The stimulated neurone releases a chemical that crosses the gap and stimulates the other neurone. Individual neurones can have synapses with many other neurones there are many possible connections that can be made. Perhaps now you realise why we respond to a particular stimulus in a number of different ways.

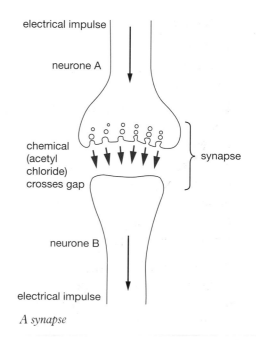

A synapse

Questions

1   What is the central nervous system?
2   Why is it important to be coordinated?
3   What is the difference between a nerve and a neurone?
4   What is a synapse? How does it work?

Reflex actions

Humans are sensitive animals. To survive we need to be able to sense change in our surroundings. We can detect things like sudden noises, flashes of light, changes in temperature, and pressure on the skin. We call these **stimuli**.

We need to be able to respond quickly to these things. For example, if someone on the hockey field shouts 'duck!' we may have to move suddenly to avoid being hit by the ball. This reaction is coordinated by our **central nervous system**. The central nervous system is made up of the brain and spinal cord. It is the control unit for all our actions.

The brain and spinal cord receive messages from sensors throughout the body. These sensors are called **receptors** and include our skin, our eyes, nose and taste buds. The messages pass along nerves to the central nervous system. This then sends messages along other nerves to muscles and other **effectors** to make them respond. The nerves are made up of special cells called neurones. **Sensory neurones** carry messages from receptors to the central nervous system. **Motor neurones** carry messages from the central nervous system to the muscles and other effectors.

Reflex actions

Sometimes animals have to react very quickly if they are not to be injured or killed. Such actions are controlled by the central nervous system and are called **reflex actions**. These are automatic responses which you cannot consciously control.

stimulus	reflex action
flash of bright light	pupil of eye gets smaller
speck of dust touches eye	eye blinks
food enters windpipe ('goes down the wrong way')	coughing
hand touches 'live' wire (electric shock)	arm moves away quickly

All these reflex actions are designed to keep you safe. There is no time to think about what to do. The body protects itself by reacting automatically. The example in the diagram shows what happens when you touch something which is very hot.

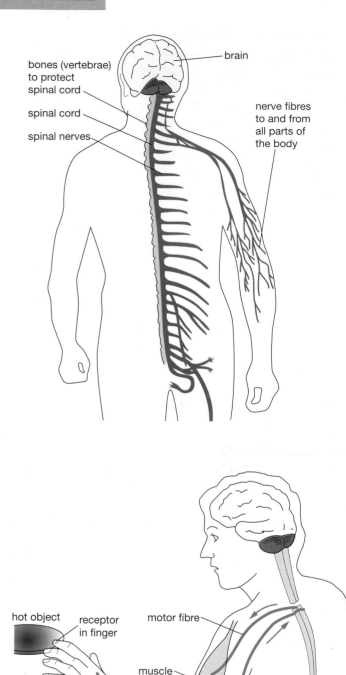

A reflex action

1 *Finger touches hot object*
2 *Receptor detects high temperature*
3 *Message sent to spinal cord through sensory fibre*
4 *Spinal cord sends message along motor fibre*
5 *Effector (muscle) responds to pull finger away*

Hormones

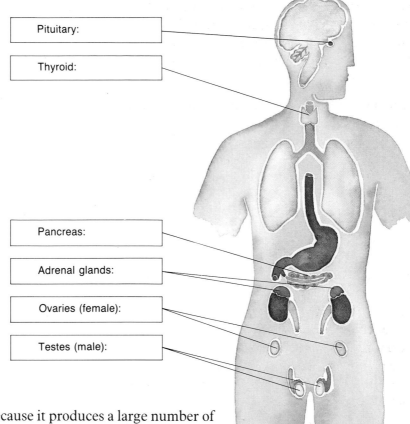

| Pituitary: |
| Thyroid: |

Hormones are chemicals produced by special glands called **endocrine glands**. Like the nervous system, hormones cause various parts of the body to react in different ways but this time the messages travel much more slowly and the effects are more general. Once released into the bloodstream from a gland, a hormone travels all round the body until it reaches **target cells**. The target cells then respond.

There are advantages in having a slow communication system. Hormones can be released into the bloodstream over a long period of time and so control the long-term changes in the body such as growth and development. The liver removes hormones from the blood when they have done their job and are no longer required.

| Pancreas: |
| Adrenal glands: |
| Ovaries (female): |
| Testes (male): |

Pituitary: called the 'master gland' because it produces a large number of hormones, many of which control the activity of other glands.

Thyroid: produces **thyroxine**, a hormone that controls growth.

Pancreas: produces **insulin** which regulates the level of sugar in the blood.

Adrenal glands: produce **adrenalin** in response to stress. This prepares the body for fighting an enemy or for running away by increasing heart beat, breathing rate and blood supply to the muscles.

Ovaries (female only): produce **oestrogen** and **progesterone** which cause body changes at puberty and control the menstrual cycle.

Testes (males only): produce **testosterone** which causes body changes at puberty.

Questions

1 Where are hormones made?

2 How do hormones travel around the body?

3 Explain why nervous 'messages' travel much faster than hormone 'messages'.

4 Diabetes is a disease where the body does not control the blood sugar level properly. Which gland is not working as it should in the body of someone with diabetes?

5 **a)** Which hormone will be released if you are chased by a bull?
b) Describe two other situations when you might produce this hormone.

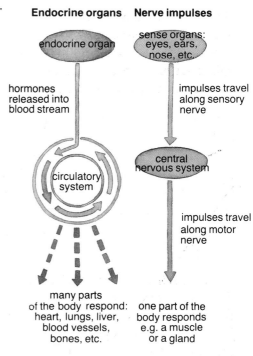

Comparing the hormone and nervous systems

The skin and temperature control

All healthy humans have a body temperature close to the average of 37 °C. Only disease or some other disorder can make it vary. The human body uses a number of control systems to keep its internal temperature steady.

The body can raise its temperature by increased activity or by absorbing more sunlight energy. We can also gain energy from hot food or drink.

The body loses heat energy from the skin by radiation and conduction. Evaporation of sweat also causes heat loss. The air we breathe out is warmer than the air we breathe in. This means we lose energy as we breathe.

For most of the time, energy losses are balanced by energy gains. Our body temperature therefore stays at 37 °C. If the surroundings heat up or cool down, or if a person does strenuous exercise, then the body's control system has to come into action.

The body's systems are controlled by the brain. If the temperature of the blood passing through the brain is incorrect, the brain sends 'information' to parts of the body which react to control body temperature. The skin plays a very important part in keeping the body temperature steady.

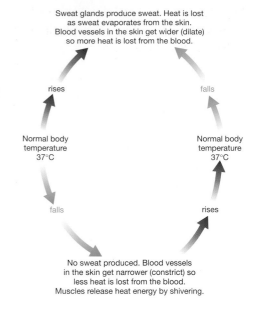

Sweat glands produce sweat. Heat is lost as sweat evaporates from the skin. Blood vessels in the skin get wider (dilate) so more heat is lost from the blood.

rises   falls

Normal body temperature 37°C   Normal body temperature 37°C

falls   rises

No sweat produced. Blood vessels in the skin get narrower (constrict) so less heat is lost from the blood. Muscles release heat energy by shivering.

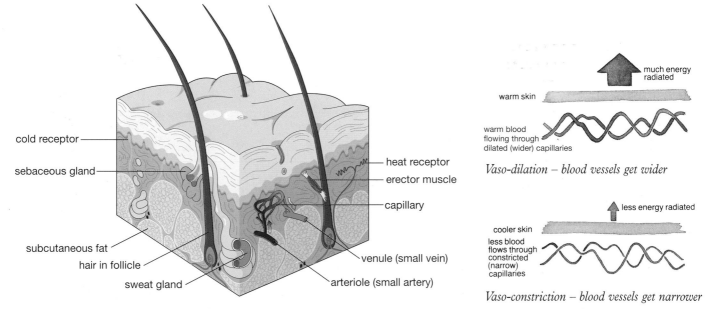

cold receptor
sebaceous gland
subcutaneous fat
hair in follicle
sweat gland

heat receptor
erector muscle
capillary
venule (small vein)
arteriole (small artery)

much energy radiated
warm skin
warm blood flowing through dilated (wider) capillaries

Vaso-dilation – blood vessels get wider

less energy radiated
cooler skin
less blood flows through constricted (narrow) capillaries

Vaso-constriction – blood vessels get narrower

Activities

1 Take your body temperature by placing a clinical thermometer under your tongue. Now take your skin temperature as accurately as you can. What difference do you notice?

2 If everyone in the class has taken their body temperature, work out the average. What is the lowest value in your class? What is the highest? What would you say if someone in the class measured their body temperature to be 45 °C?

3 Using some cotton wool, rub some alcohol on the back of your hand. (Perfume or aftershave works just as well.) What do you feel? Why?

4 Take your body temperature before and after strenuous exercise. Can you find any difference?

Microbes and disease

Many infectious diseases are caused by germs which are types of **microbes.** Microbes include viruses, bacteria, single-celled organisms called protozoa and some fungi.

Some diseases caused by microbes:

microbe	disease
virus	measles mumps hepatitis B
bacteria	whooping cough pneumonia gonorrhoea
protozoa	dysentery sleeping sickness trichomoniasis
fungi	athlete's foot ringworm thrush

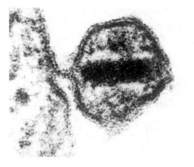

Viruses are extremely small and can only live inside the cells of other living things. They take over control of the cell contents instructing them to make more of their own kind.

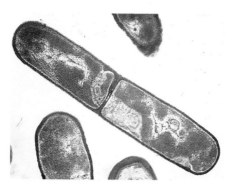

Bacteria are larger than viruses though still very small. There is a great variety of bacteria; some are very useful such as those that decompose dead organisms; others can be very harmful.

Once harmful microbes get into your body, through a cut for example, they reproduce rapidly. They feed on your body cells and produce poisonous waste called **toxins.** As the numbers increase, so more cells are damaged and more toxins are produced – you soon begin to feel ill.

Earlier in this book you read about white blood cells and their role in protecting the body against infection by microbes. Certain types of white cells, called **phagocytes**, engulf and digest microbes. Others produce **antibodies** which 'glue' microbes together making it easier for phagocytes to do their job. Yet another group of white cells produce **antitoxins** which neutralize the toxins.

When you recover from a particular disease antibodies remain in your blood system for only a short while. However, the ability to produce them in increased. This is very useful because if your body is invaded by the same kind of microbe again you are able to fight them off rapidly and so not suffer the disease. You are said to be **immune** to that disease.

Immunity to diseases can be given by **vaccination**. A vaccine is a liquid containing dead or weak microbes. When it is injected into your body you get a very mild form of disease, so mild that you probably never notice it. However, the injection is sufficient to stimulate the production of antibodies and bring about immunity to the disease.

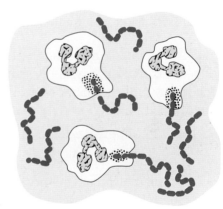

Bacteria being engulfed by phagocytes

Questions

1 Make a list of the diseases you have had. Which ones have you had more than once? Why do you think you can catch some diseases more than once?

2 Find out what diseases you have been vaccinated against. Explain what has happened inside your body as a result of these vaccinations.

3 A woman going to work in Africa had a vaccination against the serious disease cholera. She felt weak and ill for about 12 hours after the injection but then began to feel much better. Why do you think the injection made her feel ill? Why was it important for her to have the injection of vaccine?

Questions

1 The table (right) was printed on a packet of breakfast cereal.

   a)   i) How many vitamins are there in the cereal?

        ii) Why do we need vitamins?

   b)   i) Why do we need dietary fibre in our food?

        ii) Explain why these cereals are advertised as 'high fibre'.

   c) A man eats 50 g of this cereal.

        i) How much energy will he get?

        ii) How much protein will he get?

NUTRITION INFORMATION Per 100 g	
ENERGY	1650 KJ
	380 kcal
PROTEIN	8.0 g
CARBOHYDRATE	84 g
of which sugars 8 g	
starch 76 g	
FAT	0.6 g
of which saturates 0.2 g	
SODIUM	1.0 g
FIBRE	1.0 g
VITAMINS	
NIACIN	16 mg
VITAMIN B$_6$	1.8 mg
RIBOFLAVIN (B$_2$)	1.5 g
THIAMIN (B$_1$)	1.0 mg
FOLIC ACID	250 μg
VITAMIN D	2.8 μg
VITAMIN B$_{12}$	1.7 μg
IRON	6.7 mg

Nutrition label from a packet of cornflakes

2 The pulse rate and breathing rate of a young person during various activities is shown in the following table:

activity	pulse rate/min	breathing rate/min
sleeping	60	8
eating	70	17
walking to school	90	23

   a) Explain why the breathing rate is different for each activity.

   b) Explain why the pulse rate is different for each activity.

   c) What would you expect the pulse rate and breathing rate to be immediately after vigorous exercise?

   d) Describe how you would measure pulse rate.

3 A girl walking in the country accidentally touches an electric cattle fence with her hand. She immediately pulls her hand away. Explain what happens, using the following terms:

   central nervous system, muscle, receptor in skin, motor neurone, sensory neurone, spinal cord.

4 'The human blood circulatory system performs the function of transport and defence.'

   a) Name two things that are transported in the blood.

   b) What makes blood circulate in the body?

   c) Explain how blood defends the body from illness.

   d) What is AIDS? Why do people die from AIDS?

5 **a)** Describe what happens to a boy or girl at puberty.

   b) Describe what happens from the start of sexual intercourse to the successful fertilization of an egg.

   c) Name one sexually transmitted disease. Describe its cause, its symptoms and how it can be treated.

6 **a)** Explain how the body reacts when the internal body temperature starts to drop below its normal level.

   b) Old people suffer from hypothermia (very low internal body temperature) in cold weather. Suggest how hypothermia can be prevented.

7 The diagram below shows one of the tiny air sacs (alveoli) in a lung.

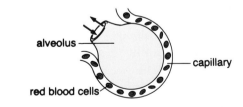

   a) What is a capillary?

   b) What gas diffuses from the alveoli into the capillaries?

   c) Name one gas which diffuses from the blood into the alveoli.

   d) Why is the surface of each alveolus i) moist ii) thin?

   e) How does smoking damage the lungs?

3　Green plants

How do plants make their food?
What travels in the transpiration stream?
How do plants reproduce?
How do plants get their water?
What are tropisms?

Green plants are very special living things. They have one big advantage over animals: they can make their own food by photosynthesis.

Most of the surface of the Earth is covered by a great variety of plants. The photographs show just a few of them. Some plants are so small you have to use a microscope to see them. The largest, the giant redwood tree, grows to over 100 metres tall and is thought to live for up to 4000 years.

Hot or cold, wet or dry, plants live in all conditions. Scientists are interested in plants. Plants provide us with food, fuel and medicines.

Garden flowers

Giant redwood, California

Pond plants

Woodland plants

Alpine plants

California prairie flowers

Questions

1   Why are plants so special?

2   Name a place where plants live which is **a**) hot **b**) cold **c**) wet **d**) dry.

3   Name five plants that provide us with food.

4   Name a fuel that comes from plants.

5   Find out the names of two medicines that come from plants.

Plant structure

Not all plants look the same as each other. A tree is very different from a primrose, and a piece of pond weed looks nothing like a rose bush. However, they all have a similar structure.

Remember, plants are living organisms too.

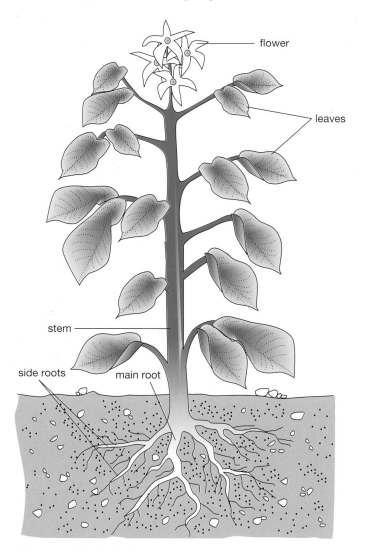

The parts of a plant

Roots hold the plant in place in the ground. They stop the plant from being blown over or washed away by heavy rain.

Roots also take in the water that is needed by the plant. Usually, roots are under the ground away from the light, so there is no point in them having chlorophyll to photosynthesize. Most roots appear white when the soil has been washed off.

The **stem** is the main support above the ground. It holds the leaves so that they can get as much light as possible for photosynthesis. Flowers usually appear at the end of the stem so that insects can get to them easily. Some plants, such as trees, have long stems. The stems of other plants, such as plantain, are very short. The leaves of plantain lie flat on the ground in the shape of a rosette.

Leaves are where the plant's food is made during photosynthesis. Leaves come in all sorts of shapes and sizes. They are usually green, although other colours exist. Whatever their colour, all leaves contain chlorophyll, the chemical that absorbs light energy from the Sun. If you look closely at a leaf, you can usually see the network of veins that carry food and water around the plant.

Flowers contain the reproductive organs of the plant. There are many types of flower, but the more obvious ones are usually brightly coloured and sweet smelling in order to attract insects, birds, and even bats. These animals come to feed on the sugary nectar stored at the base of the petals. Pollen becomes stuck to their bodies and then gets carried from one flower to another. The flowers of plants such as grasses are very small and not attractive to animals. Pollen is therefore carried by the wind between these flowers.

Questions

1 **a)** What two jobs do the roots of a plant do?
   b) Why are the roots of a plant white?

2 **a)** What is chlorophyll?
   b) Where is chlorophyll found in a plant?

3 In many plants, leaves and flowers are held above the ground by the stem. Suggest a reason for this.

4 Give two differences between flowers that are pollinated by insects, and those that are pollinated by wind.

Plants need water

All living things need water for the chemical reactions that take place inside them, to transport materials around the body and to carry away waste. In addition, plants use water to carry minerals from the soil into their roots.

How do plants take in water?

Water enters plants through the roots. The tips of roots are covered in tiny hairs. These root hairs are extensions of the outer cells of the root and grow out between the soil particles where water is held.

Water enters the roots by a process called **osmosis**. Osmosis is the diffusion of water from a weak to a strong solution through a selectively permeable membrane.

Root hairs take in water by osmosis because their cell contents are stronger than the surrounding soil and because their cell membranes are selectively permeable.

As root hair cells take in more and more water by osmosis their cell contents now become weaker than the cells next to them. So, water moves across into cells lying further inside the root.

If water continually enters a root system by osmosis it must go somewhere. Running through a plant is a miniature pipeline made of special cells called **xylem** and **phloem**. Xylem carries water and phloem carries food. It is into the xylem pipeline that water goes and as more water enters a pressure is built up. This root pressure helps move water through the plant, particularly in spring when plants begin to grow again.

Root pressure is only strong enough to push water a short distance up a stem. To get water to the top of a plant requires the 'suction' effect of transpiration.

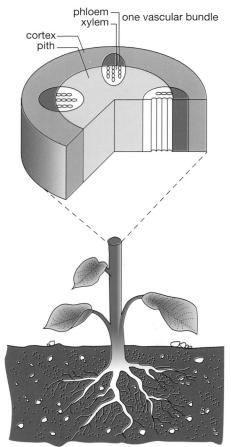

The xylem and the phloem are found all through the plant. They are held together in a vascular bundle

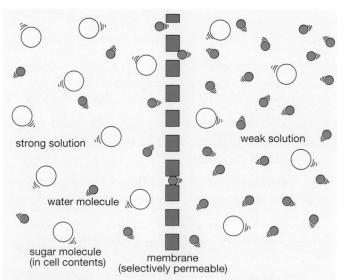

Since there are more water molecules in the weak solution, water will move through the tiny holes in the membrane into the strong solution. This continues until both sides are of equal strength.

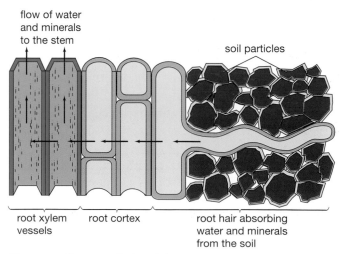

Movement of water and minerals into a root

Transanspiration: water lost from plants

Transpiration is the process by which plants lose water vapour by evaporation into the atmosphere. The water passes through tiny holes called **stomata** which are found mainly on the lower side of leaves. Two sausage-shaped **guard cells** surround each stoma and control the size of the hole. If the pressure inside the guard cells is high the stoma will be open allowing gases to be exchanged with the air. However, if the internal pressure is low the stoma will close. This will prevent any movement of gases into or out of the leaves.

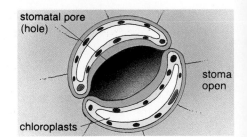
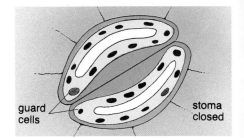

Stoma open

The rate of transpiration depends on a number of things:

- wind – on windy days water vapour will be blown away as it passes out of leaves.
- temperature – the warmer it is the more water will evaporate into water vapour.
- humidity – dry air can hold much more water than air that is wet.
- time of day – stomata usually close at night.

Stoma closed

The movement of water in the xylem from roots to leaves is called the **transpiration stream**. It appears that water is 'pulled' up the xylem tubes in a plant as water vapour is lost from the leaves during transpiration – just like a drink is pulled up a drinking straw when you suck on it. This transpiration pull is the main way in which water is transported in plants.

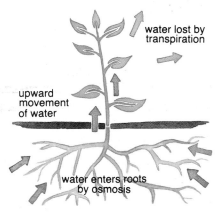

The transpiration stream

Investigating how external conditions affect transpiration

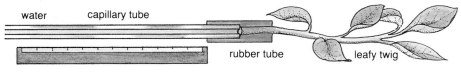

A potometer

This apparatus is called a **potometer**. It can be used to measure the rate of transpiration in a leafy shoot. This is done by measuring how far the water moves along the capillary tube in a certain time, say one minute. By placing the potometer in different conditions we can see how the rate of transpiration is affected. Look at these results.

conditions	transpiration rate mm/min
warm place	15
cold place	5
still air	8
moving air	20
dry air	10
moist air	4

Questions

1 What is transpiration?

2 What are **a)** stomata **b)** guard cells? Explain how guard cells change the size of stomata.

3 Explain how **a)** temperature **b)** wind **c)** humidity affect the speed by which a plant loses water to the atmosphere.

4 Using the results of the potometer experiment, which conditions cause plants to lose water **a)** fastest **b)** slowest?

5 Explain why a potted plant placed on a sunny window sill will soon start to **wilt.**

6 A student says 'Plants lose water in the same way as clothes dry on a washing line'. Is the student correct? Explain your answer.

Too little water

Plants and animals need water from their environment but some environments provide very little water. In the Sahara desert the average daytime temperature is about 35 °C and it only rains about every three years!

Not all places are as bad as the Sahara but even so some plants and animals have adapted to survive in very dry conditions.

Survival is only possible if animals and plants can prevent themselves drying up.

Some desert animals avoid losing too much water from their bodies by staying out of the sun. Gerbils are a good example. They live in burrows during the day and come out at night to feed when it is much cooler. They get all their water from the food they eat because there is very little water to drink.

Camels are very well adapted for desert life. When they get the chance to drink they can take in lots of water very quickly: over 100 litres in 10 minutes! They can then go for many days without drinking.

Camels' humps store food as fat. This can be used when there is no food to eat. Camels are large animals and this helps them survive. During the cold desert nights they let their body temperature drop by several degrees. During the day they heat up slowly. When the evening comes the camel's temperature is just a few degrees above normal.

Like most desert animals, camels do not waste water by producing lots of urine. Their droppings (faeces) are dry when they have been without water for some time.

The best known desert plants are cacti. They are very well adapted to dry environments. The most obvious feature is that their leaves are reduced to **spines**. The spines have a small surface area so that less water is lost. Cacti also have stomata that are closed during the hot day and open at night when water loss will be less. (The trees in Britain have their stomata open during the day and closed at night.) Cacti also have shallow root systems which spread out a long distance from the base of the stem. The roots can then take in any dew which forms on the ground. This water is stored in the green stem of the plant which becomes fleshy and even takes over the role of leaves in photosynthesis. A thick, waxy cuticle prevents water loss from the surface of the plant.

A cactus; well adapted for the desert

A camel in a desert environment

Activities

Get two or three plants of roughly the same size which are growing in pots. One should be a plant with leaves. A busy lizzie (*Impatiens*) would be ideal. Another should be a cactus or a succulent. The jade plant (*Crassula argentea*) is a good example. Water the plants thoroughly and put them on a window ledge. Look at them every day but do not water them. Make a note of any changes that you see.

Answer these questions:
1 a) Which plant wilts first?
   b) Why do think this plant lost water fastest?
2 a) Which plant needed least water?
   b) How is this plant well adapted for a dry environment?

Photosynthesis: leaves for the job

Trees, bushes, grass and flowering plants make our surroundings look attractive, but they have a much more important role. Plants are part of our food chain, so without them we would die!

Plants make their food from non-living things by a process called **photosynthesis**. The raw materials used are carbon dioxide from the air, and water from the soil. These are combined to make sugar (glucose) and starch.

Photosynthesis uses light energy from the Sun. The chemical **chlorophyll** traps this energy. Chlorophyll is contained in **chloroplasts**.

Oxygen is a product of photosynthesis. Oxygen is needed by other living things.

Leaves are the 'food factories' of plants. This is where photosynthesis takes place. Leaves are well adapted for their job. Their broad, flat, thin shape provides a large surface area, ideal for the absorption of carbon dioxide and sunlight.

Green plants need sunlight.

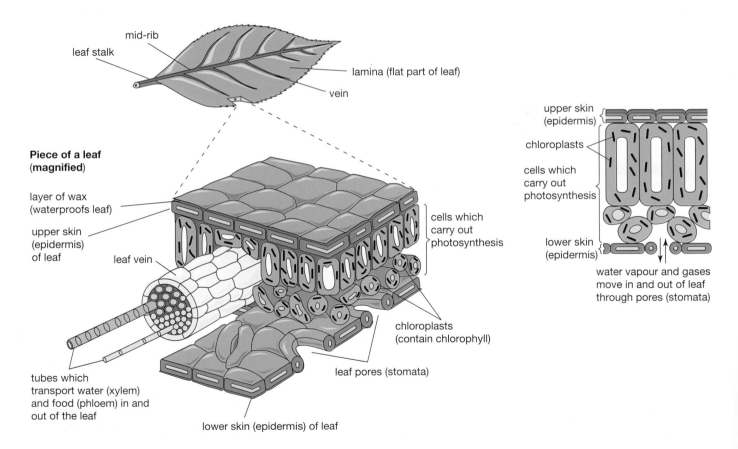

Questions

1 What is photosynthesis?

2 How does the shape of leaves help them to do their job?

3 Why is the upper surface of a leaf transparent?

4 Why do you think there are more chloroplasts in the upper part of a leaf than in any other cells?

The chemistry of photosynthesis

Photosynthesis is not one simple chemical reaction, but a series of complicated reactions. Each reaction is controlled by special chemicals called **enzymes**. (You can read about enzymes on page 33.)

We can represent what happens during photosynthesis by one equation:

$$6CO_2 + 6H_2O \xrightarrow{\text{sunlight absorbed by chlorophyll}} C_6H_{12}O_6 + 6O_2$$

carbon dioxide   water   glucose   oxygen

Carbon dioxide enters the leaf through the stomata by **diffusion**. Water is carried to the leaf in the xylem. Both carbon dioxide and water pass into the chloroplasts, where photosynthesis takes place. In the chloroplasts, light energy is absorbed by chlorophyll. Carbon dioxide and water become part of a chemical reaction that produces glucose and oxygen.

Usually, the glucose made in this way is converted to starch. This is stored for a time in the leaf until it is needed.

Oxygen is a by-product of photosynthesis. It diffuses out of the leaf through the stomata into the surrounding air.

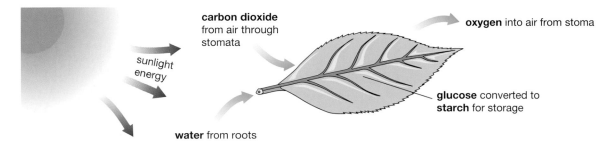

carbon dioxide from air through stomata

oxygen into air from stoma

sunlight energy

glucose converted to **starch** for storage

water from roots

Where does the oxygen come from?

For many years, scientists wondered where the oxygen came from. Was it the carbon dioxide or the water? To investigate this, scientists watered plants with special water that had been 'labelled' with atoms of oxygen that were slightly heavier than normal oxygen. These atoms were called oxygen-18 (^{18}O). Normal oxygen is oxygen-16 (^{16}O).

When the oxygen given off was tested, it was also 'labelled' with oxygen-18. This proved that the oxygen came from the water and not the carbon dioxide.

Questions

1 *Photo* means 'light' and *synthesis* means 'building up'.
   a) What chemical do green plants have in order to 'trap' sunlight?
   b) What large molecule is built up during photosynthesis?
   c) What two simple chemicals are needed for photosynthesis to take place?

   d) What gas is given off as a by-product of photosynthesis?

2 Suggest why *Potomageton natans* has its stomata on the upper surface of its leaves, not the lower. (Hint: *Potomageton natans* is a water plant that has floating leaves.)

Photosynthesis: the starch test

An easy way of finding out if a plant is photosynthesizing is to see if its leaves have produced any starch or not.

A leaf that has been kept in the dark for a day or so will not contain any starch.

Starch reacts with iodine. Iodine turns from brown to blue-black when added to starch. If a leaf contains starch, it will turn blue-black when iodine is dropped on it. This shows that the leaf has photosynthesized. If the leaf has not been photosynthesizing, it will not turn blue-black.

Testing a leaf for starch

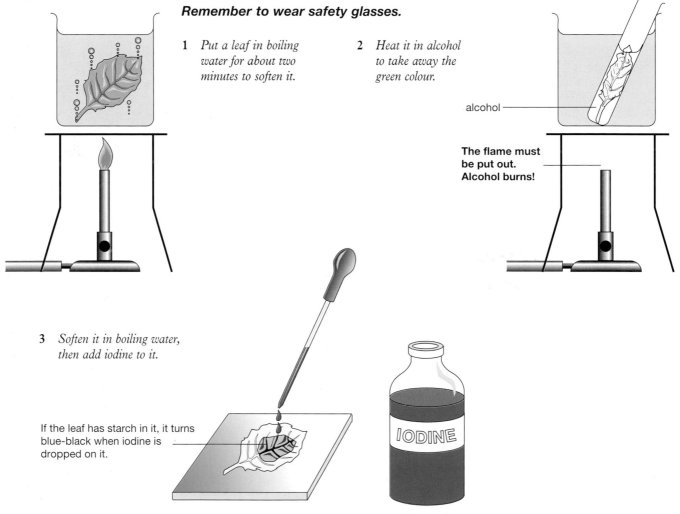

Remember to wear safety glasses.

1 *Put a leaf in boiling water for about two minutes to soften it.*

2 *Heat it in alcohol to take away the green colour.*

alcohol

The flame must be put out. Alcohol burns!

3 *Soften it in boiling water, then add iodine to it.*

If the leaf has starch in it, it turns blue-black when iodine is dropped on it.

IODINE

Questions

1 How does the starch test show that a plant has been photosynthesizing?

2 What does iodine do when added to starch?

3 During the starch test:
   a) Why is the leaf boiled in water for a short time?

b) What is the job of the alcohol?

c) Why dip the leaf in water again before adding the iodine?

4 Give one important safety precaution that must be taken during the starch test. Why is it important?

Photosynthesis: testing the equation

Now that you know the starch test, it is possible to use it to show that carbon dioxide, light, and chlorophyll are needed for photosynthesis.

We can also show that oxygen is produced, by carrying out another simple experiment.

Showing that carbon dioxide is needed

Put some soda lime into a plastic bag and carefully tie it around a leaf. (Soda lime absorbs carbon dioxide.) Leave the leaf attached to the plant. After a day, do the starch test on the leaf.

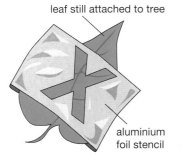

airtight seal
plastic bag
soda lime

Soda lime test

Showing that light is needed

Put a piece of foil around part of a leaf and leave it attached to the plant. After a day, do the starch test on the leaf.

leaf still attached to tree

aluminium foil stencil

Before starch test   **After testing for starch**

Showing that chlorophyll is needed

Do the starch test on a variegated leaf (a leaf that has no chlorophyll in the white bits).

Variegated leaf   **After testing for starch**

Showing that oxygen is produced

Set up the apparatus below in a well-lit place, and leave it until the test tube is full of gas. To see if the gas is oxygen, test it using a glowing splint.

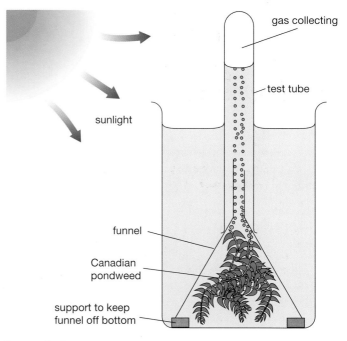

gas collecting
test tube
sunlight
funnel
Canadian pondweed
support to keep funnel off bottom

Oxygen test

Questions

1   What gas is absorbed by soda lime?

2   Describe a variegated leaf.

3   Suggest why foil is only put around part of a leaf in the experiment to show that light is needed for photosynthesis to take place.

4   Why is it important to leave the leaf attached to the plant, in the experiment to show carbon dioxide is needed for photosynthesis?

5   What does a glowing splint do when it is put into oxygen?

Tropisms

To photosynthesize successfully, plants must get as much light and water as possible. Shoots must grow upwards towards the light, and roots must grow down into the soil to get water.

Plants respond to a variety of **stimuli** by growing either towards or away from the stimulus.

These growth movements are called **tropisms**.

Tropisms are brought about by a group of plant hormones called **auxins**. Auxins are produced at the tips of roots and shoots. They affect the growth of roots and shoots. In a shoot, auxins elongate the cells just behind the tip, making it grow longer. However in roots, auxins slow down growth by stopping cells elongating.

The ivy is growing up towards the light.

Phototropism is a growth movement in response to light. If a plant grows towards the light, then it is called a positive response. Growth away from light is called a negative response.

Geotropism is a growth movement in response to gravity. Plant shoots grow upwards against the effects of gravity. They are called negatively geotropic. Roots, however, are positively geotropic.

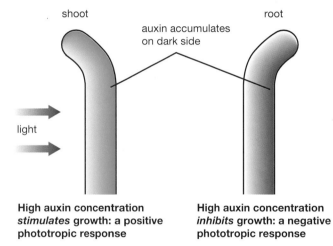

High auxin concentration *stimulates* growth: a positive phototropic response

High auxin concentration *inhibits* growth: a negative phototropic response

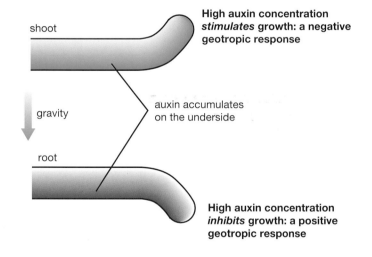

High auxin concentration *stimulates* growth: a negative geotropic response

High auxin concentration *inhibits* growth: a positive geotropic response

Synthetic plant hormones (manufactured by humans) are used by farmers and gardeners as selective weedkillers or herbicides. The most common is 2,4D. This is used as a selective weedkiller. Broad-leaved weeds absorb more of the chemical than narrow-leaved crops such as wheat. The weeds grow so quickly that they wither and die.

Questions

1 What are tropisms?

2 Name the plant hormones involved in tropisms.

3 What is the difference between phototropism and geotropism?

4 Explain these terms:
   a) positively phototropic
   b) negatively geotropic.

5 Explain how selective weedkillers work.

Soil and minerals

What is soil?

We see soil about us all the time. We see it in gardens, in fields and where holes are being dug in the roads. It is so familiar that we forget that the soil is an essential part of our environment. Without 'good' soil, farmers cannot grow crops and millions of people die. It is very important to know what soil is and how to look after it.

Soil is a mixture. It begins life as rock. The **weathering** action of wind, water and ice slowly breaks down rocks into smaller particles.

The stages of weathering can be seen in a soil profile. Try digging into the ground with a spade – the particles should get larger as you dig deeper. If you could dig deep enough, you would eventually come to solid rock.

Soils are named according to the size of the particles in them. **Clay soil** is made up of very small particles, and **sandy soils** contain large particles.

Rock particles make up the mineral or inorganic 'framework' of the soil. Mixed in with this is **humus**. Humus is organic matter made up of the remains of dead animals and plants. Humus 'binds' the rock particles together, forming soil crumbs, and prevents them from being easily blown away by the wind.

Humus improves soil quality. Most artificial fertilizers do not have its 'glueing' ability. Many of the essential **mineral salts** needed by plants come from humus.

Water covers the surface of the rock particles in a thin film. It is from this water film that plant roots take their water supply.

The spaces between the rock particles in the soil contain **air**. Any organism living in the soil requires oxygen at some time, and this is provided by the air in the soil. Air spaces are smaller in clay soil.

Soil profile

Mineral elements needed by plants

element	ions in the soil	what it is used for
nitrogen	(NO_3^- nitrate ions)	a vital part of protein for growth
calcium	(Ca^{2+} ions)	important for making cell walls
iron	(Fe^{2+} and Fe^{3+} ions)	for making chlorophyll for photosynthesis
magnesium	(Mg^{2+} ions)	for making chlorophyll for photosynthesis
phosphorus	(PO_4^{3-} phosphate ions)	a part of genes, chromosomes and cell membranes
potassium	(K^+ ions)	involved in enzyme action
sulphur	(SO_4^{2-} sulphate ions)	used in important proteins

Questions

1   A gardener tests the soil in her garden and finds it contains very little humus.
   a) What is humus?
   b) What should she dig into her soil as humus?
   c) Why is air an important part of the soil?

2   Where do plants get many of their mineral salts from?

3   A gardener finds that the cabbages in her garden have small leaves.
   a) Explain why a fertilizer rich in nitrogen would help.

Sexual reproduction in plants (1)

Flowers are the reproductive structures of plants. They contain the reproductive organs which produce the male and female sex cells or gametes. Male gametes are contained in **pollen grains**, female gametes are **ovules**.

Insects such as bees visit flowers to collect nectar and pollen for food. The flower's shape and structure means that while they are doing this the hairy body of the bee becomes covered in pollen grains. As the bee visits other flowers, pollen is transported from the anther of one flower to the stigma of another. This is **cross-pollination**. Sometimes pollen from a flower is deposited on its own stigma. This is **self-pollination**.

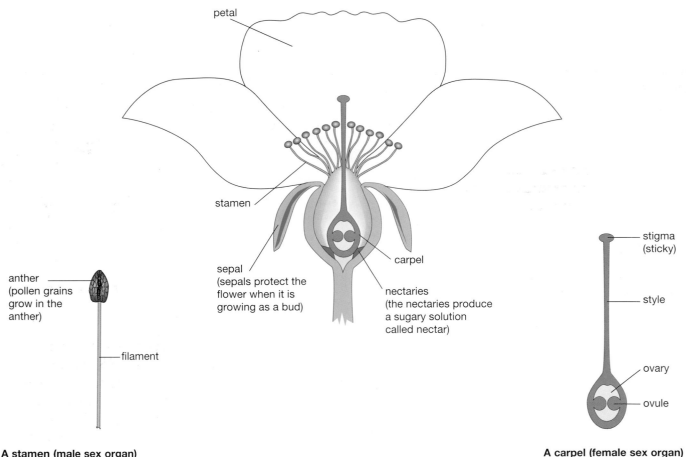

A stamen (male sex organ)

A carpel (female sex organ)

Questions

1   Why are flowers important to a plant?

2   What are **a**) male and **b**) female sex cells called in a plant?

3   Why are sepals important to a flower?

4   What is nectar? Explain why nectar is important in sexual reproduction in plants.

5   What is the difference between cross-pollination and self-pollination?

Sexual reproduction in plants (2)

Pollination

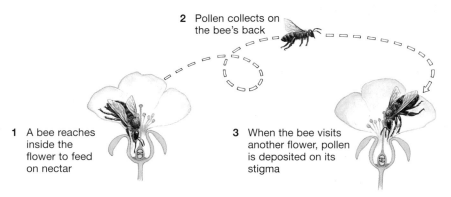

2 Pollen collects on the bee's back

1 A bee reaches inside the flower to feed on nectar

3 When the bee visits another flower, pollen is deposited on its stigma

Insect pollination

The pollen grains of some flowers are carried not by insects but by the wind. Instead of being sticky to enable them to become attached to the body of an insect, the grains are smooth and very light so that they can be blown over long distances by air currents. Grasses are wind-pollinated.

Anthers and stigmas hang outside the flowers to help release and capture pollen. Wind-pollinated flowers are usually much smaller than insect-pollinated flowers and are not so attractive to look at. These hazel catkins are a good example.

Fertilization

Fertilization, as in animals, involves the joining of the nuclei of the male and female gametes. It happens like this …

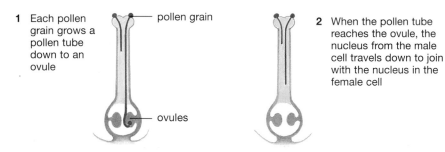

1 Each pollen grain grows a pollen tube down to an ovule

— pollen grain

— ovules

2 When the pollen tube reaches the ovule, the nucleus from the male cell travels down to join with the nucleus in the female cell

Hazel catkins: wind-pollinated flowers

Activities

Take a flower from an insect-pollinated plant. Use tweezers and small scissors to separate the parts of the flower. Count the number of petals, anthers and carpels. Cut an ovary open and try to find the ovules inside.

Questions

1 How does an insect carry pollen from one flower to another?

2 What other way can pollen get from one flower to another?

3 Describe **four** differences between a wind-pollinated flower and an insect-pollinated flower.

4 What is fertilization? Describe the process of fertilization in plants.

5 A student was using a microscope to look at pollen grains taken from two different flowers. Some pollen grains were small and very smooth.
The others were larger and had a spiky, sticky surface. Which pollen came from hazel catkins? Explain your answer.

Sexual reproduction in plants (3)

After fertilization most of the flower dies, only the ovary survives. Inside the ovary the fertilized ovules grow and develop into seeds. A **seed** consists of a tiny embryo plant enclosed with a supply of food in a tough protective coat or **testa**.

As seeds grow the ovary grows as well. The fully developed ovary with its seeds inside is called a fruit. Bean pods, sycamore 'helicopters', dandelion 'parachutes' and plums are good examples of fruits. Their job is to help scatter or **disperse** the seeds to new areas so that the new plants won't be overcrowded when they grow or **germinate**.

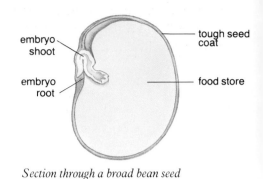

Section through a broad bean seed

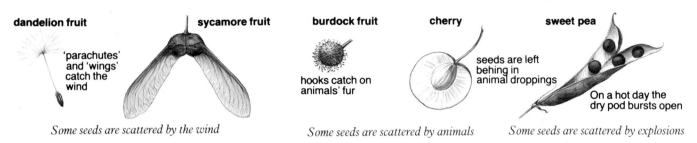

Some seeds are scattered by the wind

Some seeds are scattered by animals

Some seeds are scattered by explosions

Germination

Seeds need water, oxygen and a suitable temperature before they begin to germinate. That is why many plants don't begin to grow until the spring when it gets warmer and the soil is neither frozen nor hard and dry.

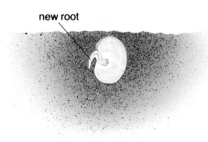

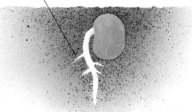

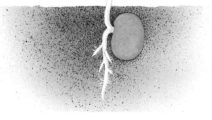

*Water is absorbed and the seed swells. The testa softens and the young root (**radicle**) grows down into the soil.*

Root hairs develop to enable more water and dissolved mineral salts to be taken into the seed. Water helps prepare food reserves for use by the growing plant.

*The young shoot (**plumule**) grows upwards through the soil, develops leaves and soon begins to make new food by photosynthesis.*

Questions

1 Why are seeds dispersed away from the parent plant?

2 Explain how the fruit of the sycamore is designed to carry seeds away from the parent plant.

3 Explain why fruits like cherries are brightly coloured and sweet tasting on the outside and why the seed inside has a hard coat.

4 Design an experiment to show that cress seeds need water and warmth before they will germinate.

Asexual reproduction: propagation

Some plants, as well as being able to reproduce sexually by producing seeds, are also able to reproduce by growing new parts which can live as separate plants. This is a form of **asexual** reproduction since no gametes are involved.

Strawberries send out special stems called **runners** that spread over the ground. At the tips of these stems a bud forms which grows into a new plant.

Strawberry plants

Rhizomes are underground stems. Couch grass has a rhizome. Notice how roots and leaves grow at intervals along it.

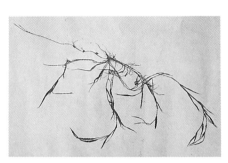

Couch grass

Tubers are also underground stems. Potatoes are an example. Although swollen with food, the potato, like any stem, has buds – the 'eyes'.

Potato tuber

Bulbs are large underground buds with swollen leaves full of food.

Onion bulb

Corms are often mistaken for bulbs but instead of being a bundle of swollen leaves they are a flat, swollen stem.

Crocus corm

Humans have made use of the plant's ability to reproduce asexually. Stocks of identical plants can be built up by taking **cuttings**. Many of our well-known house plants like geraniums are produced from stem cuttings. Others such as the African violet are grown from leaf cuttings. Taking cuttings is really quite simple, all you do is place a piece of cut stem or a leaf into some moist compost and leave it to develop its own roots. Some are much easier than others. The new plants must be looked after very carefully.

Fruit and rose growers use the technique of **grafting**. A V-shaped cut is made into the stem of a healthy plant (the **stock**). Then a stem from another plant of the same type (the **scion**) is trimmed and fitted into the cut. The two parts are then tightly bound together and sealed. After a few weeks the two parts will have grown together. Grafting is useful if lots of a popular fruit or flower are needed for sale.

Micropropagation – tissue culture

Some types of plant can be grown from a tiny piece of plant containing only a few cells. This is called **tissue culture**. Tissue culture is useful because thousands of identical plants can be grown from just a few cells. The technique can be used in the production of vegetables such as carrots and potatoes, and especially for producing ornamental plants such as orchids, where each individual plant is very valuable.

The carbon cycle

All living things contain the element carbon. In our ecosystem, carbon circulates from the environment into living things and then back again. This is known as the **carbon cycle**.

At the same time as carbon is circulating, oxygen is also passing in and out of living things. The carbon cycle and the **oxygen cycle** are connected.

Photosynthesis and respiration

We have seen that plants photosynthesize. This can be written as a word equation.

Carbon dioxide + Water + Energy → Food (sugar) + Oxygen

Respiration is how animals and plants release energy from their food. (You can read more about this in Chapter 9.)

The simple word equation for respiration can be written

Food (sugar) + Oxygen → Carbon dioxide + Water + Energy

Notice that the respiration equation is the opposite of the photosynthesis equation. In a balanced ecosystem, photosynthesis and respiration will keep the oxygen and carbon dioxide levels in the atmosphere steady.

Unfortunately it is not that simple. For example, large quantities of carbon are trapped as the fossil fuels coal, oil and natural gas. (See Chapter 4.)

When we burn these fuels carbon dioxide is given off. At the same time lots of the world's jungles and forests are being cut down. This means that there are fewer plants to photosynthesize and produce oxygen. These two activities may be upsetting the balance of the gases in our environment and so scientists must continually monitor what is happening in our atmosphere.

Every time you light a gas cooker you are releasing carbon atoms which were locked up millions of years ago!

Questions

1 A student says 'Respiration is the opposite of photosynthesis'.
   a) Write the word equations for respiration and photosynthesis. Use these to show what the student means.
   b) Give one reason why respiration is not *exactly* the opposite of photosynthesis.

2 A large aquarium contains fish and green plants.
   a) What gas is given out when the fish respire?
   b) What gas is taken in when the green plants *photo-synthesize*?
   c) What gas is given out when the green plants *photo-synthesize*?
   d) What gas is taken in when the fish *respire*?
   e) The gases dissolved in the water are perfectly balanced during the day. What happens at night?

3 A large forest is cut down. The branches are then burnt. Give two reasons why this may increase the amount of carbon dioxide in the atmosphere.

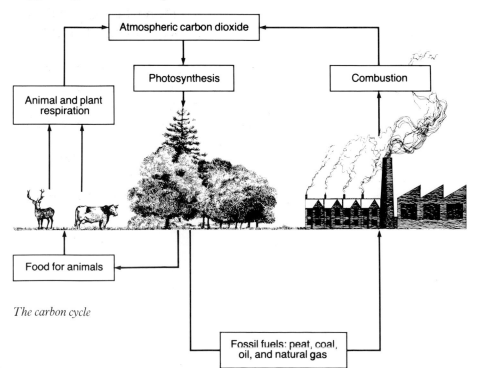

The carbon cycle

1 The diagram shows a cell.

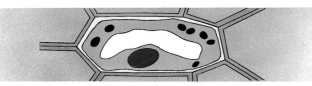

a) Does the cell come from a plant or an animal? Give two reasons for your answer.
b) Each plant and animal cell has a 'nucleus'. What does the nucleus do?

2 The diagram shows a flower.

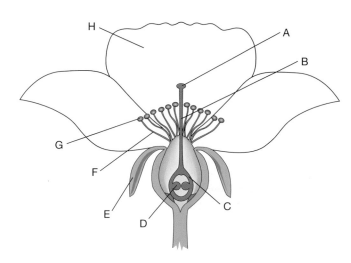

a) Name the parts of the flower labelled A-H.
b) Which part:
   i) makes males sex cells?
   ii) attracts insects?
   iii) is sticky, to collect pollen from insects?
c) Name one insect that pollinates flowers.

3 Your family allotment has not produced very good crops for a few years, in fact only peas and beans seem to show any real growth.

You have a supply of chemicals enabling you to make up a variety of solutions containing known mineral salts. Devise an experiment to test whether or not the allotment soil is deficient in one or more mineral salts.

4 The diagram shows a leaf photosynthesizing – taking in raw materials and producing certain substances.

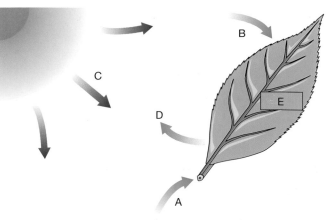

a) Name the raw materials A and B.
b) Name the products D and E.
c) What do the arrows labelled C represent?
d) How could you show a leaf was photosynthesizing?

4 Water is lost from the leaves of plants by a process called transpiration.
a) How does water get out of a leaf during transpiration?
b) List three things that can affect the rate of transpiration from a leaf.
c) Give one way in which a plant can try to reduce the rate of transpiration.

5 a) Some fruit trees will only bear fruit if their flowers are pollinated by pollen from a different variety of tree.
   i) Explain what is meant by pollination.
   ii) Explain how pollen can reach one fruit tree from another.
b) Some fruit trees can be propagated by taking cuttings.
   i) What is meant by 'propagation by taking cuttings'?
   ii) Why is a tree that grows from a cutting exactly like its parent?

What is variation and why is it important?
How do we inherit characteristics?
What is a species?
How have living things evolved?

The people in the photograph, and you, belong to one type or species of animal. Scientists call this species *Homo sapiens*.

As you can see, the people have lots of things in common. For example, they have the same general body shape and their faces have similar features.

However, even though they are all easily recognizable as humans, there are lots of small differences between them.

People, like all living things, inherit their characteristics from their parents. Some of your characteristics come from your mother and some come from your father.

This is why there are variations in every species of plant and animal. These variations are very important and have helped *Homo sapiens* in particular to evolve over millions of years into a very successful species.

Activities

1 Cut out photographs of five famous people from newspapers or magazines.
List five things that help you recognize that they are all humans.
List five things that tell you they are all different individuals.

2 Find two plants **of the same species**. These could be two trees, two garden plants or even two houseplants, but they must be of the same type.
List three differences. You could consider leaf shape, leaf size, bark pattern, flower shape, height of plant, thickness of stem and many other things.

Variation

Every species has characteristic features of shape and structure by which it can be recognized and identified. Look at your classmates and you should recognize that they have similar features to you; features that make them human beings.

However, you should also be aware that individual students in your class are not exactly the same as you or each other. Different hair colour, height, weight and skin colour are examples of differences that we call **variation**.

Variation in humans

Characteristics that are distinct, such as being able to roll your tongue or having ear lobes are examples of **discontinuous variation**. You either have the characteristic or you don't.

Other characteristics are not so easily separated, such as the difference in human body weight. If you measure and record the height of your classmates, you should find that they form a complete range. This is an example of **continuous variation**.

Are you a roller or a non-roller?

You are likely to find a small number of very short people and a few very tall ones, but most will be bunched around the average height. We call this a **normal distribution**.

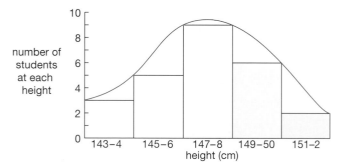

Do you have ear lobes or not?

Activities

Make a family tree of your relatives and try to find out about their characteristics. Ask about things like hair colour, eye colour, height, colour blindness, tongue rolling ability etc.

Changes in the environment such as different amounts of food, light and space can have an effect upon the way individuals develop. Height and weight can be influenced by what sort of food we eat and how much we eat. Our skin colour is dependent on how much sunlight we are exposed to. A typical European on holiday in a sunny country will change colour for a short while!

This sort of variation is often referred to as **acquired variation**.

Can you see where your characteristics came from?

Passing on information

Inside the nucleus of each one of your cells are structures called **chromosomes**. These are fine threads of material which carry 'bits' of information about what you look like. These bits of information are called **genes** and each one controls one or more characteristics that you have inherited from your parents.

Human cells have 46 chromosomes altogether. These are paired off, making 23 pairs. Each chromosome in a pair is like its partner and carries information about the same feature although this information may not always be the same. For example, one of a pair of chromosomes with information about hair colour may carry the instruction 'be blond' while the other may carry the instruction 'be dark brown'. These pairs are called **homologous pairs** of chromosomes.

We inherit one chromosome in a homologous pair from our mother and the other from our father.

When gametes are made the number of chromosomes must be halved. Homologous pairs are separated inside the sex organs so that the sperms and eggs, pollen and ovules only possess one of each pair. At fertilization the two 'half sets' are put together to make a full set of pairs in the new individual.

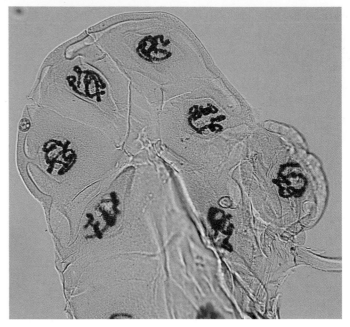

Cell showing chromosomes dividing

As a new baby or seed grows, more cells must be made, each one having its own set of chromosomes carrying just the same information as the original fertilized cell. The stages of cell division are shown in the diagram below. (Only four chromosomes are shown to make things simpler.)

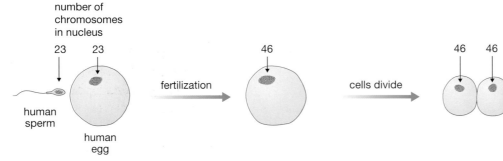
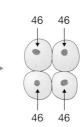

Fertilization and cell division

Questions

1   What is the difference between a chromosome and a gene?

2   A mouse has 40 chromosomes in each of its cells.
    a) How many homologous pairs does it have?
    b) How many chromosomes are there in the sperm of a male mouse?

3   A pea plant has 14 pairs of chromosomes in each of its cells.
    a) How many chromosomes will there be in a pollen grain cell?
    b) How many chromosomes will there be in an ovule?
    c) Explain why a pea plant grown from a seed will have 28 chromosomes in each of its cells.

Patterns of inheritance

Many of our features, for example hair colour and eye colour, are controlled by a pair of genes. The colours of your hair and eyes were determined at fertilization when the nucleus of your father's sperm fused with the nucleus of your mother's egg. The passing on of characteristics from one generation to the next is called **heredity**. The study of heredity is called **genetics**.

Let us think about hair colour. At fertilization the two genes for hair colour which come together could carry the same instructions, for example 'be blond'. In this case the person will have blond hair. When the two genes are the same we call the person **homozygous** for the character.

Of course the two genes could carry different instructions, for example 'be blond' and 'be dark brown'. In this case, one of the genes will usually be **dominant**. This means that one gene will dominate the other and will control the character. The gene which is not dominant is called **recessive**. Now 'dark brown' is dominant over 'blond' so the person will have dark hair. When two genes are different we call the person **heterozygous** for the character.

If both parents are heterozygous for a particular character then their children could inherit genes in a number of different combinations. A useful way of showing the possible gene combinations is to use a Punnett square (named after the famous geneticist Reginald Punnett).

The Punnett square drawn here shows the possible outcomes of a cross between two parents heterozygous for eye colour. B represents the gene for brown eyes and b the gene for blue eyes. The gene for brown eyes is dominant over the gene for blue eyes – this is why it has a capital letter!

When we look at a person we cannot always tell what sort of genes they have. For example a brown-eyed person could have two genes for brown eyes (homozygous) or one gene for brown eyes and one gene for blue eyes (heterozygous). To avoid confusion we must use two more terms: **phenotype** – the outward appearance of the person, and **genotype** – the kind of genes the person has.

Hair colour is controlled by genes. Each of these blond girls' cells contains two genes for blond hair

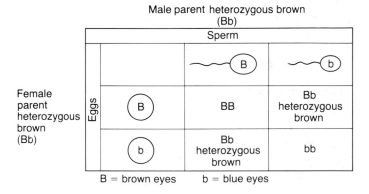

A Punnett square

Questions

1 **a)** What does *homozygous* mean?
b) If an egg carrying a gene for blue eyes is fertilized by a sperm carrying a gene for brown eyes, will the person be homozygous or heterozygous for eye colour?

2 **a)** Write down your *phenotype* for i) hair colour ii) eye colour.
b) Write down the *genotype* for a blue-eyed person.
c) Why couldn't you be sure about the genotype of a brown-eyed person?
(*Hint:* Use the words dominant and recessive in your answer.)

3 Draw a Punnett square to show the possible outcomes of a cross between a brown-haired woman and a blond man. (Use the letter B for the brown hair gene which is dominant and b for the recessive blond gene.)

4 A person with brown hair has it dyed red. Have they changed their genotype? Explain your answer.

Boy or girl?

Genetics is involved in determining what sex we are. Chromosomes that determine whether we are male or female are called **sex chromosomes**. There are two types, one is called an X chromosome and the other, shorter one is called a Y chromosome. Females have two X chromosomes, males one X chromosome and one Y chromosome.

At gamete formation all the eggs from the mother will carry X chromosomes. However, only half the sperms of the father will carry an X chromosome, the other half will carry a Y chromosome.

If a sperm carrying an X chromosome fertilizes an egg the child will be female. On the other hand if the sperm contains a Y chromosome the fertilization will result in a male child.

It is the sperm therefore which determines the sex of children. There is a 50 per cent chance of a boy and a 50 per cent chance of a girl. This is why the human population, like many others, is roughly half male and half female.

Sex-linked inheritance

Genes that are present on the X chromosome are more likely to affect a male than a female. This is because the Y chromosome is shorter and therefore some gene positions will be missing. The gene for colour blindness is recessive and is on the X chromosome in a position which is unfortunately not present on the Y chromosome. As a result the message on the gene cannot be dominated and the male will be colour blind. In females, colour blindness is rare. A woman will only be colour blind if both X chromosomes carry the same recessive gene.

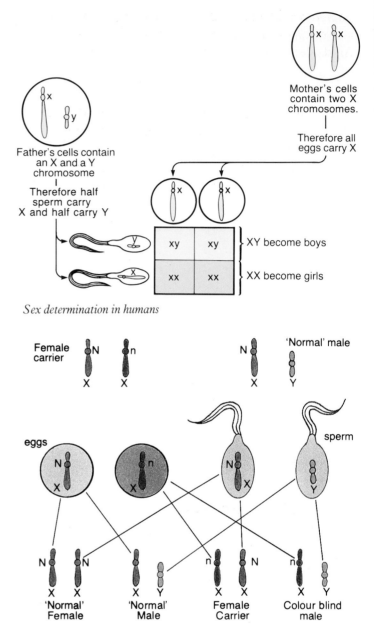

Sex determination in humans

N = gene for Normal vision
n = gene for Colour blindness

Genetics and colour blindness

Questions

1 Write down the phenotype (male or female) and the genotype (XX or XY) for **a)** yourself **b)** your teacher **c)** your best friend.

2 It is possible to find whether an embryo in the womb of a pregnant woman has XX or XY chromosomes.
    a) Explain how this tells whether the baby will be a boy or a girl.
    b) Suggest one reason why this information may be important to a parent.
    c) Do you think parents should be able to find out the sex of their baby before it is born? Explain your answer.

3 Write down *five* problems encountered by colour blind people.

Mutations

Sometimes when cells divide, the structure of a chromosome may become altered or a gene copied incorrectly. These changes are called **mutations**. All descendants of an individual having a mutation are called **mutants**.

Chromosome mutations

When gametes are formed in the sex organs there is a chance that changes in the number or structure of chromosomes can take place. Some chromosomes break in two places and the piece in the middle falls away taking its genes with it. This will seriously affect the development of an organism.

On other occasions, homologous pairs of chromosomes do not separate properly and both go into the same gamete. This kind of chromosome mutation is the cause of **Down's syndrome**. People having this condition possess three 'twenty-first' chromosomes instead of two. This possession of an extra chromosome causes physical and mental problems for the sufferer.

A chromosome mutation can cause a woman to produce an egg with 24 chromosomes instead of 23. If the egg is fertilized the baby develops Down's syndrome.

Gene mutations

A chemical change which alters the message carried by a single gene is called a gene mutation. Gene mutations that occur in gamete-producing cells are transmitted to all the cells of the offspring and may therefore affect the future of the species.

Sickle-cell anaemia is a disease in which the red blood cells become sickle shaped. Victims of the disease suffer all the problems associated with extreme oxygen shortage such as weakness and eventual heart failure. The anaemia is caused because the sickle-shaped red blood cells contain an abnormal form of haemoglobin called **haemoglobin-S**. Haemoglobin-S is very inefficient at carrying oxygen.

A gene mutation causes haemoglobin-S to be produced rather than normal haemoglobin.

The formation of 'new' genes by mutation has probably had a significant effect upon the range of plant and animal species that live on Earth today.

Questions

1 Explain the difference between a chromosome mutation and a gene mutation.

2 What are mutants? Name a mutant condition that you have read about.

3 Warts, moles and other skin blemishes are caused by mutations of skin cells. These features are not passed on from one generation to the next, they die when the person dies. Why is it, therefore, that haemophilia (a disease that prevents blood-clotting) is inheritable?

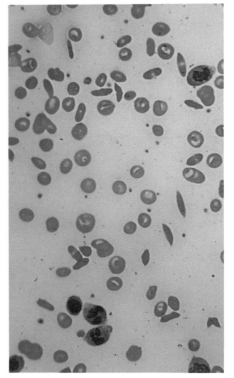

Blood with sickle cells

What is a species?

A **species** is a population of organisms which can breed together and produce fertile offspring. Usually individuals of different species will not interbreed. If however breeding does take place then the offspring are likely to be sterile. This is because the species will have different numbers of chromosomes in their cells.

The horse and the donkey are different species but because they are very similar they can interbreed. The offspring of the horse-donkey cross is called a **mule**. A mule is sterile and cannot produce baby mules. The only way to get mules is to cross a horse with a donkey.

A mule: healthy but sterile

How are new species formed?

Before a new species can be formed it is necessary for a large group of animals or plants to be split up into separate groups. These groups must be **isolated** from each other so that there is no possibility of genes being exchanged between them. Breeding will continue within the groups producing more generations. Over thousands of years, mutations and variations will produce organisms which differ so much from the original group that they form a new species.

Geographical isolation

Populations of animals or plants may become split up by natural barriers like mountain ranges, rivers and seas. The finches on the Galapagos Islands in the Pacific Ocean are a good example. Mainland finches are all the same: they have short, straight beaks for crushing seeds. On the Galapagos Islands there are thirteen species, differing mainly in the shape of their beak. It would seem that the original population of finches was split up and isolated on the separate islands. Each smaller group adapted to feeding on the different types of food found there.

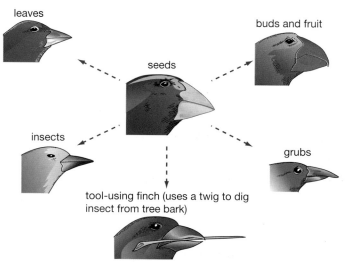

leaves

buds and fruit

seeds

insects

grubs

tool-using finch (uses a twig to dig insect from tree bark)

Some of the species of finch found on the Galapagos Islands

Behavioural isolation

Courtship before mating is important in the behaviour of many animals. It helps members of the same species to identify one another and to choose a healthy mate. Birds use visual and sound signals. Among animals, smell is an important factor in recognition.

Individuals that are not able to produce the appropriate signal or not produce the signal at the right time are not going to attract a mate.

A bird that sings the wrong song or has the wrong colour feathers will not be able to breed.

A peacock displaying to attract a mate.

Evolution: the theory

The theory of evolution offers an explanation for the production of new species from earlier, simple life forms over millions of years.

In his book 'On the Origin of Species', Charles Darwin explained his theory of how evolution could come about by a process of **natural selection**. He received support from another naturalist, Alfred Russel Wallace, who had come to the same conclusions as Darwin at about the same time.

Darwin had investigated the plants and animals in different parts of the world when he was on board a survey ship, *HMS Beagle*. He was particularly impressed by the wildlife on the Galapagos Islands in the Pacific Ocean.

Despite some strong opposition following the publication of his book in 1859, Darwin's theory has stood the test of time and is today widely accepted.

Charles Darwin (1809–1882)

The theory of natural selection

The Darwin/Wallace theory of natural selection can be summarized as follows:

1　Within any population of living things there is variation.

2　Even though all species produce large numbers of offspring, natural populations stay fairly constant.

3　There must be a struggle for survival within populations.

4　Some individuals are better adapted to their surroundings. These are more likely to grow and reproduce passing on their advantage. Others without it, will die.

So, particular organisms have been naturally selected from their population because they are better adapted to the environment than their fellows.

Alfred Russel Wallace (1823–1913)

Natural selection in action

There are a number of examples of natural selection that have been studied during the past 50 years.

Cepaea nemoralis is the common land snail found in woods, fields, hedges, sand dunes and rough ground all over Europe. The shells of this species show considerable variation. The background colour may be various shades of brown, pink or yellow and the shell may have up to five dark bands around it. Both colour and banding is **inherited**. Snails which do not blend in with their surroundings are easily spotted by birds who will eat them. In woods with only a little undergrowth, banded snails are at a disadvantage and will be selected out, but in undergrowth and on rough ground banded snails are well camouflaged and are so be more likely to survive. Snails with unbanded shells will be easily seen by birds and are therefore likely to be eaten!

Which of these snails will be selected out?

Selective breeding

Since civilization began, thousands of years ago, humans have been selectively breeding domesticated animals and plant crops. Darwin used evidence from this **artificial selection** to account for evolution by natural selection.

New varieties of animals and plants are produced by deliberately selecting those individuals that have desired characteristics and breeding from them.

All dogs, even breeds as different as the Great Dane and Chihuahua, belong to the same species and have descended from the wolf.

Pug

Irish wolfhound

Wolf

Chiahuahua

Great Dane

The danger of inbreeding

Continued breeding of closely related individuals is common, especially in the production of 'show' animals like cats and dogs. Unfortunately this practice can lead to infertility and reduced resistance to disease. This is why it is important to investigate the family tree or **pedigree** of an animal before buying it.

Questions

1 Explain the difference between *natural* selection and *artificial* selection.

2 In what ways do humans struggle to survive? (*Hint:* it may help to think of people in developing countries.)

3 A modern cow produces several gallons of milk each day. Suggest how farmers have artifically selected cows to give so much milk.

4 Champion male race horses are often 'put to stud'. Race horse owners then pay thousands of pounds to have their female horses mated with the ex-champion. Explain why.

5 What do you think you should look for in a pedigree before buying a dog?

Artificial selection breeds faster racehorses.

Evolution: the evidence (1)

Evidence from fossils

Fossils are any sort of remains of a once-living organism preserved in the rocks of the Earth's crust.

Under special conditions the entire body of an organism may be preserved after it dies. Insects trapped in the sticky sap of ancient trees can now be observed embedded in amber. In the early part of the twentieth century frozen woolly mammoths were found in Siberia. Their meat was still edible after thousands of years in the deep freeze!

Total preservation of organisms is rare; usually the soft body parts decompose leaving only the bones or shells. When these become covered with sediment, sand or gravel, they produce fossils a few thousand years later when the sediment becomes rock.

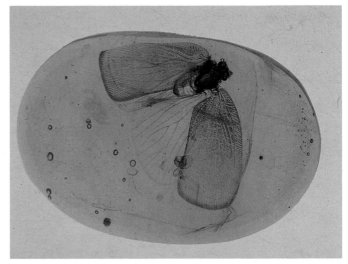

Fossilized insects

The Grand Canyon – 2000 million years of history

The Grand Canyon in Arizona is the deepest crack in the Earth's surface, about a mile deep.

The rocks of the canyon contain thousands of fossils. Each layer of rock provides evidence of the order in which animals and plants appeared on Earth over the past 2000 million years.

Near the top, fossils of reptiles such as dinosaurs can be found. Further down, the number and complexity of fossil species decreases. Halfway down, the fossils of fish first appear and below three quarters of the way down there are no signs of life at all.

Activities

Making 'fossils'

1   Put some soft, moist sand into a small dish.

2   Push an object such as a shell or a bone into the sand so that a clean impression is made.

3   Make a cardboard frame around the impression making sure it is both carefully sealed and pushed well into the sand.

4   Pour Plaster of Paris into your mould and leave to it set.

5   Carefully remove the plaster cast from the mould and you have a 'fossil'.

Of course, this is not a *real* fossil but the activity shows how some fossils may have formed millions of years ago.

Grand Canyon, USA

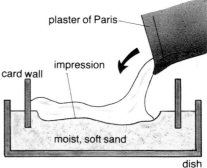

Making 'fossils'

Evolution: the evidence (2)

Evidence from anatomy

If you compare the skeleton of one mammal with another it is easy to spot that some parts of the body have a similar structure. Notice in the diagram how the limbs of various mammals share the same basic structure even though they have completely different functions and are different shapes.

This provides evidence that animals like these evolved from a common ancestor.

Other similarities can be recognized in the bodies of different species of mammals. For example the blood circulatory system and the digestive system are very similar in each type of animal.

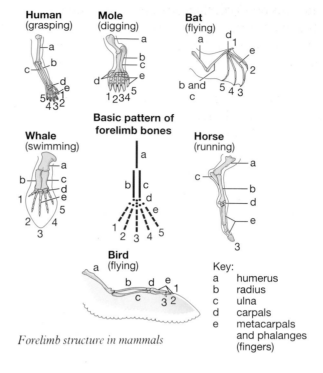

Forelimb structure in mammals

Evidence from geographical distribution

The distribution of animals on the oceanic islands provides strong support for the theory of evolution.

An oceanic island is one which has never been connected to the mainland. Usually they are formed by the eruption of volcanoes lying deep beneath the sea. As molten rock from the volcano cools down it solidifies and forms an isolated home for any organism that can get there from the mainland.

Study of the life on oceanic islands shows that many of the species on them had relatives on the mainland but over thousands of years they have evolved so that they are now very different.

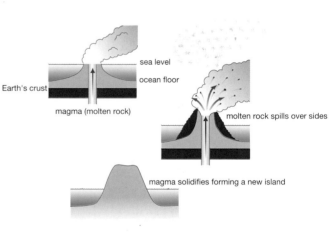

Formation of oceanic islands

Questions

1 The 'limbs' of the bat and the whale are called **homologous** because they have the same basic structure.

    a) Look at the diagrams on this page and list *two* similarities between them.

    b) Why does the similarity between the bones of the bat and the whale suggest that they have evolved over millions of years from the same type of animal?

2 Hawaii is a volcanic island.

    a) Explain how islands like Hawaii form.

    b) Suggest two ways that animals could have reached Hawaii from the mainland.

    c) Suggest two ways that plants or their seeds could have reached Hawaii.

There are more humans on Earth than any other large animal. They live in the hottest deserts as well as the coldest parts of the planet. People have climbed the tallest mountains, explored the deepest seas and even travelled to the Moon. In fact our species, *Homo sapiens*, has evolved into the most successful species on Earth. This is not because we are the strongest or the quickest but because we are the most intelligent. We can plan, communicate in speech and writing, and can make and use tools. We need to ask 'what did we evolve from?'

Where did the human race come from?

Our ancestors are not alive today. There is some convincing evidence to support the view that humans and the apes of today, the gorilla, orang-utan and chimpanzee, share a common ape-like ancestor that lived 50 million years ago.

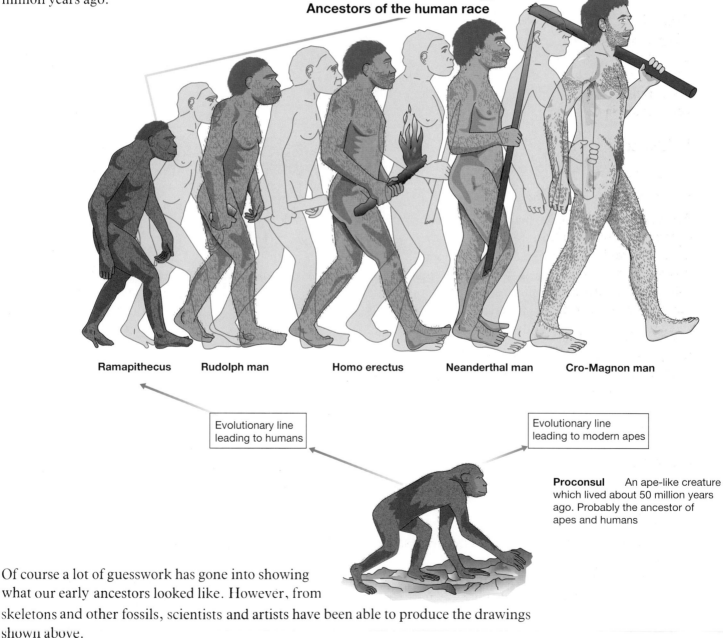

Ancestors of the human race

| Ramapithecus | Rudolph man | Homo erectus | Neanderthal man | Cro-Magnon man |

Evolutionary line leading to humans

Evolutionary line leading to modern apes

Proconsul An ape-like creature which lived about 50 million years ago. Probably the ancestor of apes and humans

Of course a lot of guesswork has gone into showing what our early ancestors looked like. However, from skeletons and other fossils, scientists and artists have been able to produce the drawings shown above.

We will never know why a group of ape-like creatures moved down from the trees onto the grassland millions of years ago. One possible explanation could be that a small group was driven out of the forests by the rest because of competition for food and space.

On the grasslands our ancestors had no protection and so environmental pressures selected only those individuals who were better adapted to their new surroundings. Over millions of years a new kind of animal, *Homo sapiens*, evolved.

Being able to think quickly was a big advantage, those that couldn't soon starved or got killed by animals. Natural selection allowed a large brain case and brain to evolve.

early ancestor

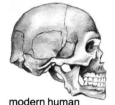

modern human
Notice how a large space for the brain has evolved

Feet slowly changed from gripping structures, necessary in trees, to more rigid body parts suitable for heel and toe walking and running.

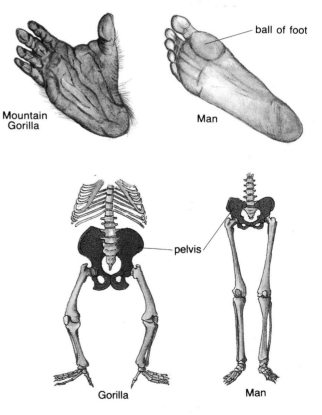

In humans the pelvis is held directly above the legs. This provides a more upright posture and more efficient movement. Notice how your knees and feet are close together when you stand upright. Unfortunately there are some disadvantages to this arrangement of bones. A large number of people today suffer from back problems such as slipped discs and some women have difficulty in giving birth because of the relatively narrow pelvic girdle.

Questions

1 Why is it wrong to say that humans have descended from apes? Write a better statement about the link between humans and apes.

2 Why was it an advantage for our early ancestors to stand upright when they moved from the forests to the grasslands?

3 Suggest how Zulus and other native Africans are adapted to survive in hot climates.

4 Explain how our large brains have enabled us to dominate all other large animals. (*Hint:* think about hunting, farming, building etc.)

5 What sort of inventions have made humans successful?

The human pelvis is much shorter. This allows the knees and feet to be close together when walking or running.

Questions

1 The diagram shows some butterflies.

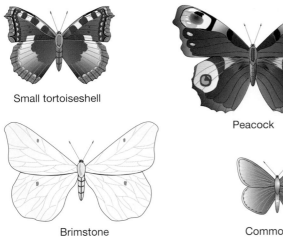

Small tortoiseshell

Peacock

Brimstone

Common blue

a) Give *three* way in which the butterflies differ from each other.

b) The peacock butterfly looks like it has eyes on its wings. The brimstone butterfly looks like a dead leaf when it lands on a plant.

Suggest how these characteristics might help the butterflies survive.

2 Sex cells are called *gametes*. Gametes contain *chromosomes* which pass information on from one generation to the next. In animals, the male gamete is called a *sperm*.

a) Name the gamete made by female animals.

b) This diagram represents a sperm.

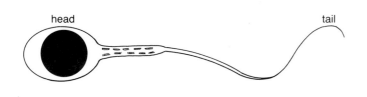

head

tail

    i) What is the tail for?

    ii) Where are the chromosomes?

c) The sex of humans is controlled by X and Y chromosomes. Women have XX chromosomes and men have XY chromosomes.

    i) What type or types of chromosome could you find in a sperm?

    ii) What type of chromosome could you find in a female gamete?

d) Draw a diagram showing how sex is inherited in birds.

3 The photographs below show a cart-horse, used for pulling heavy loads, and a racehorse, used for sprinting.

Both horses are varieties of the same species. They have been bred using artificial selection to enable them to do their different jobs.

a) How is the cart-horse adapted to do its job?

b) How do you think breeders have used artificial selection to produce the cart-horse?

c) Modern racehorses have been produced by breeding from mares (females) and stallions (males) that can run fast. Give two reasons why a person should check the pedigree of a racehorse before buying it.

d) How would you prove that racehorses and cart-horses are varieties of the same species?

4 A homozygous blond man has a heterozygous brown-haired wife. Show that there is a fifty/fifty chance that their first child will have blond hair. Use the symbols B for brown and b for blond. (Brown is dominant.)

5 Humans have evolved into the most successful of all the mammals. Their large brain lets them plan, make tools and machines, and communicate through language.

a) How does thinking help the Inuit to survive in very cold conditions?

b) How have machines helped to improve our food supply?

c) If you visit a foreign country but do not know the language it is difficult to make yourself understood, or to understand what people are saying. Suggest how you could communicate with people in such circumstances.

What is the environment?
Where does our food come from?
What happens when living things die?
How easily can the balance of nature be upset?
How do populations affect each other?

Building

Quarrying

Farming

Waste disposal

'**Environment**' is a scientific word for 'surroundings'. You are probably reading this in your school environment or your home environment.

Your environment provides you with such things as air to breathe, water to drink, and a suitable temperature in which to live. These are the **physical** or non-living parts of the environment.

Your life is also affected by other **living** things. These could be the people in your class, your family, your pets and even the bacteria in the air.

Living things, together with their physical environment, form an **ecosystem**. Lots of things go on in an ecosystem, especially feeding.

Food passes from plant to animal, and from one animal to another along a **food chain**. Food chains are linked together in food webs. Each plant or animal in one chain is likely to be a link in another chain. **Food webs** contain more information about what eats what in an ecosystem.

We have to be careful not to upset the balance in our environment. The photographs show some of the ways in which our environment can be changed.

Questions

1   Describe the environment in which you are reading this book.
Give examples of the living and non-living parts of your environment.

2   Describe the environment you would choose for an ideal summer holiday.

3   Your local council opens a large rubbish tip. How would it affect your environment if you lived nearby? How would it affect your environment if you were a seagull? (Hint: seagulls eat scraps.)

Food chains: an introduction

Green plants make their own food during photosynthesis (see page 124) using energy from sunlight. Any living thing that makes its own food is called a **producer**. Green plants are therefore producers.

Animals, on the other hand, cannot make their own food. They must get their food by eating plants or by eating other animals. Animals are called **consumers** because they eat or consume other living things.

Animals that eat plants are called **herbivores**. Rabbits are herbivores. They eat grass, cereals, carrots, lettuce and many other plants.

Animals that eat other animals are called **carnivores**. A fox is a carnivore. It feeds on animals such as insects, mice, birds and rabbits.

Some animals feed on a diet that includes both plants and other animals. These are called **omnivores**. Badgers are omnivores. They feed on things like grass, fruit, slugs, worms and rabbits.

Each plant and animal is a link in a **food chain**. Energy, in the form of food, passes from producers to herbivores to carnivores.

Here is an example of a food chain.

A badger; an omnivore

producer   primary consumer   secondary consumer

A food chain with three links

Notice there are three links in this food chain. Not all food chains have three links. Some have more like this one.

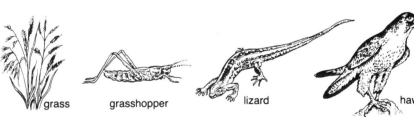

grass   grasshopper   lizard   hawk

A food chain with four links

Questions

1 What is **a)** a producer **b)** a consumer? Give one example of each.

2 Are you a herbivore, a carnivore or an omnivore? Explain your answer.

3 Explain why all living things depend on sunlight for their food.

4 A student went to study a local pond. In one part of the pond she noticed tadpoles scraping at some pond weed. In another part she saw a water beetle holding a tadpole in its jaws.

    a) Construct a food chain for the pond.
    b) How many links are there in this chain?
    c) Suggest another food chain linking the following pond organisms:
    water fleas, perch, microscopic plants, stickleback.

5 Construct **a)** a long **b)** a short food chain ending with **you**.

Food webs

Single food chains do not give us a full picture of the feeding relationships between plants and animals. We all know that rabbits do not feed entirely on lettuce and foxes do not eat rabbits all the time, and you don't live on just fruit!

If we were to trace every food chain involving lettuce, rabbits and foxes we would end up with lots of interconnecting food chains. This is called a **food web**.

See how complicated it all can get with even a few living things in a food web!

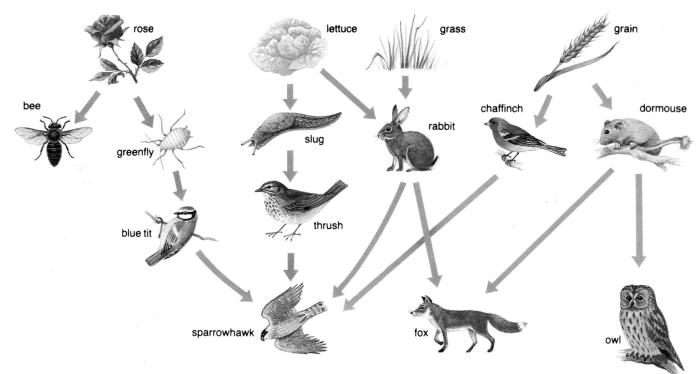

A food web

See how complicated it can get with even a few living things in a food web!

Questions

1   Look closely at the food web above then:
   a) Write down a food chain with   **i)** two links   **ii)** three links   **iii)** four links.
   b) Write down the names of the herbivores.
   c) Which carnivore has the most varied diet? Explain your answer.
   d) Suggest one way in which the sparrowhawk can   **i)** help   **ii)** hinder a gardener.

2   Rose growers often spray their roses with insecticide to kill greenfly.
   a) Explain why this can upset the food web.
   b) Suggest a way in which rose growers could control the numbers of greenfly without using any chemical sprays.

Producers and consumers

The first link in a food chain is always a producer. As you have seen, producers are plants which photosynthesize.

The producers in aquatic (water) ecosystems are mainly algae.

The producers in land ecosystems are much more varied.

Herbivores that feed on producers are called **primary** or **first-order consumers**. Mice, rabbits, horses and sheep are primary consumers.

Carnivores that feed on primary consumers are called **secondary** or **second-order consumers**. **Tertiary** or **third-order consumers** feed on secondary consumers, and so on up the food chain. Herring, owls, foxes, cats and dogs are carnivores that could be secondary or tertiary consumers. It all depends on what they are eating at the time!

Look at this food web for the North Sea.

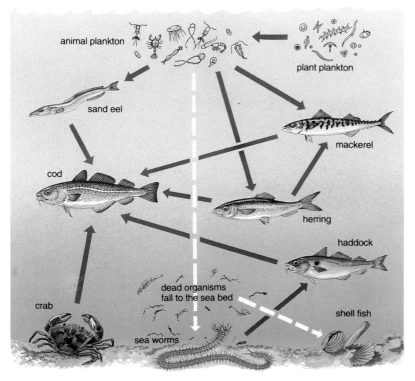

The producers in this food web are plant **plankton**. Plankton live near to the surface of the sea. Animal plankton are the primary consumers. There are many examples of secondary and tertiary consumers, such as herring and mackerel.

Questions

1 What is the difference between a primary and a secondary consumer?

2 Use the North Sea food web to answer the following questions.
   a) Name   i) the producer
   ii) the primary consumer
   iii) a secondary consumer.
   b) Give one occasion when a mackerel is   i) a secondary consumer   ii) a tertiary consumer.
   c) Explain why the cod can be called a quaternary (fourth-order) consumer.

3 A student was telling her friend about some things she saw happening in and around a local pond. She said that she had seen tiny water fleas eating algae; a heron with a perch in its beak; minnows eating water fleas; and a perch chasing minnows around the pond.

   a) Write down   i) the shortest   ii) the longest food chain.
   b) Name   i) the producer
   ii) the primary consumer
   iii) the secondary consumer
   iv) the tertiary consumer in the longest food chain.

93

Scavengers and decomposers

So far we have looked only at carnivores that feed on other living animals. Many animals avoid being eaten. They live on and reproduce in order to keep their species going. However, all animals die sometime, so what happens to their dead bodies?

In every ecosystem there are consumers that feed only on the dead remains of others. These animals prevent the environment from getting cluttered up with dead bodies and waste. They also ensure that materials are recycled in ecosystems. These consumers are of two types, **scavengers** and **decomposers**.

A scavenger is an animal that feeds on dead animal or plant remains. Snails in a pond eat dead fish. Crows feed on dead insects, birds, rabbits, and anything that might be killed on the roads by passing cars and lorries. Seagulls are often seen scavenging on rubbish tips for scraps of our discarded food. Of course these animals can fill other 'slots' in food chains as well – they're not scavengers all the time. Pond snails eat algae, crows eat corn, and seagulls eat fish; it all depends upon what is available at the time.

Decomposers don't eat dead animals and plants. They digest them by releasing enzymes on to the remains to break them down into simpler substances. Some of this digested material is then absorbed into the decomposers' own cells. Fungi and bacteria are decomposers. These organisms are important in the cycling of materials in the soil environment. Producers then take up the materials which decomposers have made, use them to grow and so make them available for living animals in food chains.

Bracket fungus on a tree

Questions

1 a) What is the difference between a scavenger and a decomposer?
b) What do scavengers and decomposers have in common?

2 In many large towns and cities foxes can be seen at night rummaging through litter bins. In the countryside foxes can be seen hunting, catching, and eating small animals such as rabbits.
Explain why a fox can be called both a scavenger and a secondary consumer.

3 People often put out bread for birds to eat. In winter this bread usually disappears quickly.
However, in summer the bread may lie around for several days, eventually becoming covered in mould (a fungus).
Suggest reasons for these observations.

Activities

1 Look carefully in your garden or around your school grounds for either a dead animal or a pile of faeces left by an animal. Make a note of its position, its size, and the date you found it. **Do not touch the animal or faeces**.

Over a period of several days or weeks note any changes that take place to your sample. You may like to consider the following:

- Has it changed its position?
- Has it changed in appearance?
- Has it changed in size?
- How long did it take to disappear completely?
- Was its disappearance due to the activity of a scavenger or decomposers?

Investigating food webs

A group of school students were studying a corner of their school field. They identified dead leaves, woodlice, millipedes, and centipedes. Their teacher asked them to investigate the feeding relationships between these organisms.

The students set up five dishes as shown below. Each dish was covered with a lid with several holes in it. The dishes were put in a cool, dark place and left for a few days.

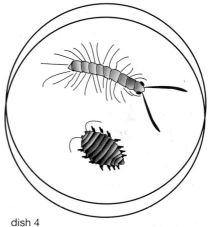

dish 3

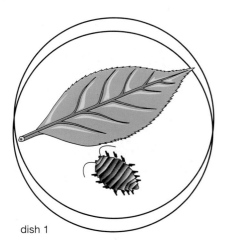

dish 1

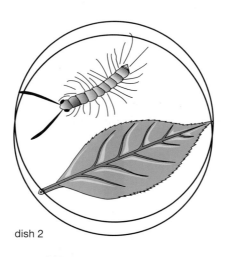

dish 2

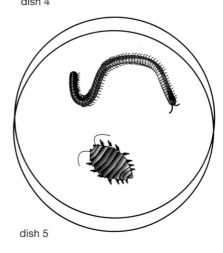

dish 4

dish 5

The students presented the results of their investigation in the form of a table. This is what they wrote.

dish	organisms inside	what had happened
1	dead leaf and woodlouse	part-eaten leaf and live woodlouse
2	dead leaf and centipede	dead leaf and dead centipede
3	dead leaf and millipede	part-eaten leaf and live millipede
4	woodlouse and centipede	part-eaten woodlouse and live centipede
5	woodlouse and millipede	dead woodlouse and dead millipede

Questions

1 Which of the organisms in the dishes is **a**) a producer **b**) a primary consumer **c**) a secondary consumer **d**) a predator **e**) a herbivore **f**) a carnivore?

2 Write down one food chain. Explain how you used the evidence from the investigation to do this.

3 Write down a food web linking all the organisms.

4 Suggest reasons why the students **a**) covered the dishes **b**) put holes in the lids **c**) put the dishes in a cool dark place.

Ecological pyramids (1): a pyramid of numbers

When you study an ecosystem you will probably realize that there are usually more producers than consumers. For example, if you studied this food chain:

grass → rabbit → fox

you may well find that there were 1 000 000 individual grass plants, 15 rabbits and 1 fox.

It is sometimes useful to have this extra information about a food chain. If the single fox was killed or moved away from the area we may want to know how the rabbit population was affected and, in turn, how this change affected the number of grass plants, especially if the grass was a food crop!

This extra information can be shown as a sort of bar chart. The length of each bar represents the number of organisms forming that link of the chain.

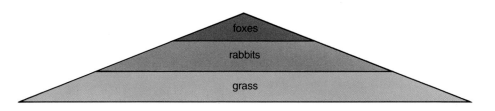

Another way of presenting the same information would be:

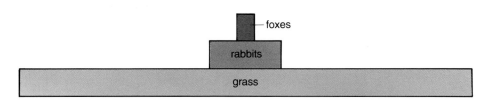

Notice the shape of each diagram. They are both called **pyramids of numbers**.

Not all pyramids are as neat and tidy as the ones shown above. Sometimes the producer may be a single, large plant such as an oak tree. Living and feeding on this oak tree could be thousands of caterpillars. Small birds feed on the caterpillars. In turn, hundreds of fleas could be feeding on the blood that they suck in small amounts from the birds.

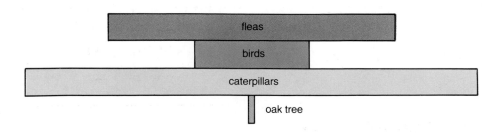

Questions

1 How does a pyramid of numbers get its name?

2 What does the length of each bar in a pyramid of numbers represent?

3 Explain briefly why pyramids of numbers can be many different shapes.

4 Draw a pyramid of numbers for this information taken from a survey of a woodland ecosystem

    1 elm tree
    400 caterpillars
    9 sparrows

96

Ecological pyramids (2): a pyramid of biomass

Biomass is a word used to describe the mass of living material in an ecosystem.

If we measured the mass of organisms in each level of this food chain:

grass → rabbit → fox

we may well find that the mass of grass was 500 kg, the mass of rabbits was 50 kg, and the mass of foxes was 10 kg.

These figures can also be shown as a bar chart.

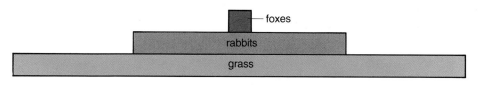

Notice that we get another pyramid – a pyramid of **biomass**. Ideally we should measure dry biomass but this is often not practicable because the organisms have to be killed and dried out. Good estimates can be made from wet (living) biomasses.

If we use this method of showing the feeding relationships in an oak tree you will notice that we get a different picture to that shown on the opposite page.

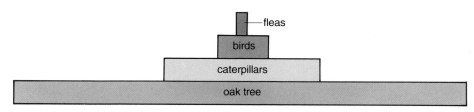

This looks much more like a true pyramid now!

Questions

1 What is biomass?

2 What is your **wet** biomass?

3 Give one similarity and one difference between a pyramid of numbers and a pyramid of biomass.

4 A group of students were studying this food chain that they had observed in a corner of their school field:

leaves → woodlice → centipedes

They collected all the leaves, woodlice and centipedes they could find and weighed them. The results are shown in the table.

    a) Use this information to draw a pyramid of biomass for this food chain.
    b) Why is it important that the students **weigh** all the organisms in this food chain?
    c) Suggest what might happen if another 10 grams of woodlice were added to the food chain.

organism	biomass
leaves	4.5 kg
woodlice	5 g
centipedes	1 g

Energy flow through ecosystems (1)

Carbon, oxygen, nitrogen, and water circulate in the environment. Even though they continuously change from one form to another, these materials stay in roughly the same proportions within ecosystems. Energy, however, does not cycle. Instead it flows through ecosystems in a straight line.

Producers convert the light energy from the Sun into chemical energy in sugar molecules. Some of this energy is used by plants in respiration, while the rest is stored as starch or used to build other chemicals like protein and fat. When consumers feed on plants they release this stored energy by digestion and respiration. They can use it for activities such as movement. Some energy, however, will be 'locked up' in the animal's body in fat and protein. This whole process is repeated at each link in a food chain. In the end all the energy is 'lost', usually as heat, to the environment. The trapping of energy from the Sun by producers maintains a continuous flow of energy through ecosystems.

Let's follow the flow of energy through a food chain which is important to humans:

grass → bullock → human

What happens in one year to the energy from the Sun when it falls on to just one square metre of grass?

Questions

1 a) How much energy is   i) 'locked up' by the square metre of grass each year   ii) taken up by the bullock each year from a square metre of grass?
b) Calculate the percentage of energy from the grass taken up by the bullock.
c) Explain why this figure is so small.

2 a) How much energy is   i) used by the bullock in growing   ii) lost in faeces and urine   iii) 'locked up' in the bullock?
b) Calculate the percentage of energy from the Sun that eventually gets 'locked up' in the bullock.

3 a) Make a list of the parts of the bullock that humans usually feed on.
b) Explain why humans take up only a small proportion of the energy 'locked up' in the bullock. Suggest where the rest might go.
c) Suggest where the energy might go after a human has taken it from the bullock.

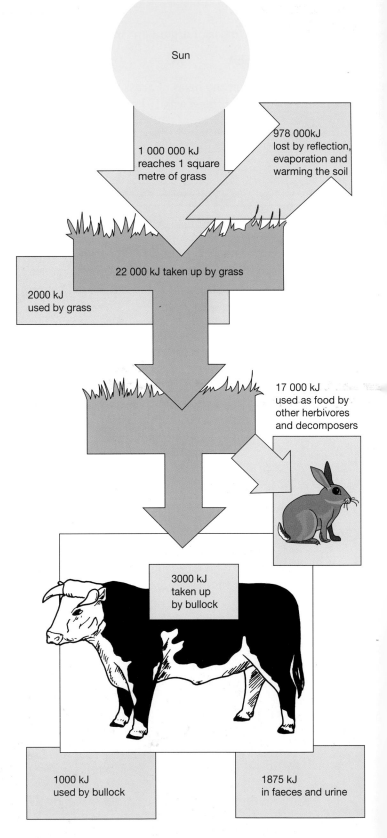

Energy flow along a food chain in one year

By now you should understand that the transfer of energy along a food chain is very inefficient. In most food chains there is usually a high loss of energy between each link:

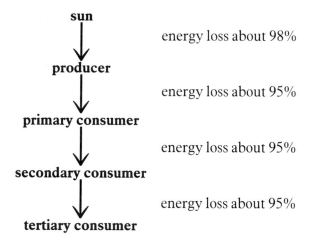

```
                sun
                 │
                 ▼              energy loss about 98%
             producer
                 │
                 ▼              energy loss about 95%
          primary consumer
                 │
                 ▼              energy loss about 95%
         secondary consumer
                 │
                 ▼              energy loss about 95%
          tertiary consumer
```

This energy loss could be cut down if people were to eat food from further down the food chain. Eating plants instead of the animals that feed on them makes better use of the available energy. This is why cereals are grown in such large quantities all over the world, particularly in North America, Russia, and China.

The main cereals grown are wheat, barley, oats, rye, maize, and rice. All these plants started out millions of years ago as wild grasses. Early humans selected the seeds that they gathered from these grasses and used them to grow 'new' varieties. Gradually this artificial selection led to the evolution of the modern cereals that we see today.

Wheat is one of the most common cereals produced in the world today. More than 300 million tonnes are produced each year. It can be used for making:

flour . . .   . . . pasta . . .   . . . and of course breakfast cereals.

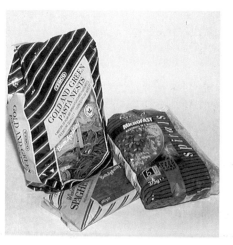

Competition

In an ecosystem there are always more organisms produced than can ever survive. Only those best adapted to their environment will survive. This is one of Charles Darwin's important observations, which helped him to develop his theory of evolution. Competition takes place between organisms of the same species and between organisms of different species.

What do plants compete for?

Plants make energy available to other organisms by 'trapping' it from sunlight. Plants must therefore try to get as much light as they can in order to make as much food as possible. This competition for light can be seen in a wood. The faster growing trees usually win the race!

Water and mineral salts are essential for plant survival. Food cannot be made without them. Plants with root systems that spread deeper and wider in the soil will be more likely to survive at the expense of those with smaller roots.

Bright, sweet-smelling flowers attract insects. The more insects that visit a flower, the more chance the plant has of pollinating other flowers and therefore reproducing itself.

Trees competing for food and light in a woodland environment.

What do animals compete for?

Food and water are vital to animals for survival. The more food and water an animal can get, the better its chances of survival. Animals, unlike plants, can move from one place to another. So animals can hide from predators or shelter from bad weather.

Like plants, animal species can only survive if individuals can find a suitable mate. The bigger, fitter males usually win the battle to mate with the females.

In many species males fight for a mate.

Questions

1   Why do living things need to compete with each other?

2   How do plants compete for a) light b) water?

3   Why are animals more likely to survive a period of drought than plants?

4   List three things that animals complete for.

5   A student set up an experiment. She made some thick gravy, poured it into a saucer and left it to cool in the open air. After a day, the saucer was covered in clingfilm and put in a warm place for a few more days. When she next looked at the saucer, the student noticed that colonies of bacteria and fungi had completely covered the gravy. Where two colonies of bacteria had grown close together, one colony appeared to be bigger than the other.
   a) What had the bacteria been competing for?
   b) Suggest why one colony had grown bigger than the other.

Some terms to know

All living things live in places that are best suited to their needs. The place where an animal or plant lives is called a **habitat**. Bluebells are usually found in woodland, so the habitat of bluebells is woodland. Sometimes the word **microhabitat** is used to describe a small part of a habitat. A rotting log in a woodland habitat provides a microhabitat for many plants and animals. Microhabitats usually provide different conditions from the main habitat.

If an organism is to live successfully, its habitat must contain food, shelter, and a place to breed.

A **species** is group of organisms of the same type that live and breed successfully together to produce fertile offspring. Individuals of different species will not usually interbreed. If breeding does take place the offspring will probably be sterile. The horse and the donkey are different species. However, they can interbreed because they are similar to each other. The offspring of this cross is called a mule. Mules are sterile and so cannot produce baby mules.

Organisms do not live their lives on their own. They usually form breeding groups. These groups are called **populations**. Populations of animals and plants are made up of individuals of different ages, which live in habitats which are most suitable for them. For example, a population of wood mice is made up of young and old mice living in a woodland habitat.

A habitat is usually occupied by a number of different plant and animal populations. This collection of organisms living together in one habitat is called a **community**. A wood is a good example of a community. It is made up of populations of trees, shrubs, grasses, ferns, birds, wood mice, squirrels, insects, and many more kinds of plants and animals. There are close links between members of a community. These links are usually to do with food. Many organisms are the food of others living in the same community. There are many complex food webs in a woodland habitat.

Sometimes a community may contain more of one particular species than any other. These are called **dominant species**. A wood dominated by oak trees is called an oak wood. Oak woods are very different habitats from beech woods or birch woods.

A woodland habitat

Questions

1 What is your habitat?

2 Make a list of the people that make up your school community.

3 **a)** What is a species?
   b) If the horse and the donkey are different species, why can they breed?
   c) How do you know that the horse and the donkey belong to different species?

4 What is a community?

tail (helps the squirrel to balance)

strong teeth

feet have 'fingers' and 'toes' for gripping

The squirrel is well adapted to life in a woodland habitat.

A closer look at a woodland community

The colonization of bare earth, followed by a build-up of communities, is called **succession**. A wood is usually a stable community, the result of the final stage of plant succession. Such communities are full of many different species of both plants and animals.

In a wood the plants are arranged in four layers.

- The tree layer consists of large trees with big trunks. Their leaves form a canopy covering the rest of the wood.

- The shrub layer contains shrubs such as hawthorn and bramble.

- The field layer is made up of herbaceous or non-woody plants like grasses, ferns, and woodland flowers such as primrose and bluebell.

- The ground layer covers the surface of the soil. Mosses and lichens are found here.

The layering of plants in a wood is called **stratification**.

Animals move freely between layers. For example, squirrels search for food in the ground layer but move to the tree layer to sleep and breed. Birds nest in the tree layer and feed on berries in the shrub layer.

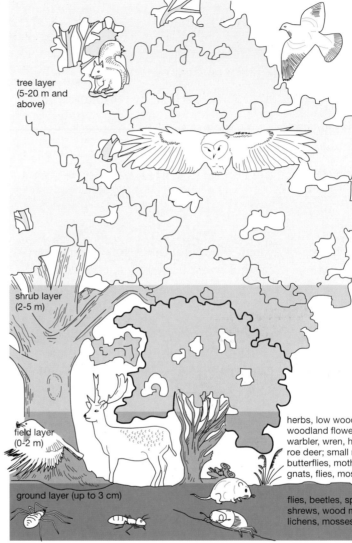

tree layer (5-20 m and above)

dominant species e.g. oak; some co-dominants, e.g. sycamore; birds e.g. barn owl, sparrowhawk, wood pigeon, magpie, jackdaw, crow, songthrush, chaffinch, great tit, blue tit, jay, woodpecker, nuthatch, tree creeper; grey squirrel; many insects, larvae (caterpillars) of winter moth

shrub layer (2-5 m)

several species e.g. hawthorn, blackthorn, dogweed, elder, dog rose, buckthorn; birds e.g. robin, blackbird, pied flycatcher, redstart, woodpecker, nuthatch, tree creeper; many insects as in field layer; grey squirrel

field layer (0-2 m)

herbs, low woody plants, tree saplings, woodland flowers, ferns; birds, e.g. coal tit, warbler, wren, hedge sparrow; fallow deer, roe deer; small mammals, e.g. dormouse; butterflies, moths, bees, wasps, hoverflies, gnats, flies, mosquitoes, beetles, spiders

ground layer (up to 3 cm)

flies, beetles, spiders, grasshoppers, voles, shrews, wood mice, harvestmen, ants; lichens, mosses, liverworts, low herbs

Questions

1 Sometimes the tree layer is called the canopy layer. Why do you think this is?

2 a) What is an herbaceous plant? **b)** Name two herbaceous plants.

3 List **a)** two animals **b)** two plants of the ground layer.

4 Why do you suppose grasshoppers are not found above the field layer?

5 Explain why:
a) Woodland plants like the primrose always flower in spring.
b) Bluebells have a store of food in their bulbs. They can burst into growth early in the year.
c) Ivy is a plant that climbs up the trunks of large trees.
d) Mosses are delicate plants that quickly dry out. However, they grow well in the ground layer of a wood.

A pond community

A pond is a usually stable community full of aquatic life. There is more life in shallow water, where the sunlight can reach the bottom.

A pond community can be divided into four areas or zones.

- The **marsh zone** consists of plants with their roots firmly anchored in wet mud.

- The **swamp zone** is occupied by plants whose roots are submerged and rooted in mud. Their leaves and flowers are above the water. Some stems are tall and upright, others are short with leaves floating on the surface.

- The **deep water zone** is made up of plants that have weak root systems. These plants can be easily uprooted by animals or by sudden movements in the water.

- The **open water zone** is where floating aquatic plants are found. The water is too deep for plant roots to reach the bottom.

Animals can move between the zones, but they tend to spend most of their time within one or two zones. Each animal is well adapted for survival in its zone.

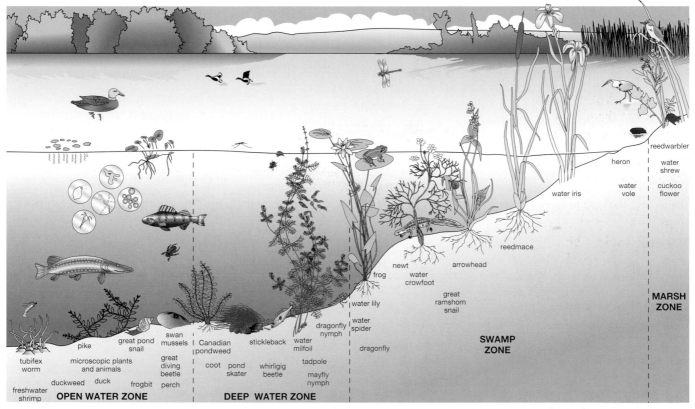

Questions

1 Name the four zones that a pond community can be divided up into.

2 List **a)** two animals and **b)** two plants of the swamp zone.

3 Why do you think newts and frogs are not found in the open water zone?

4 Adult ducks move between the zones. However ducklings stay close to the marsh and swamp zones. Suggest a reason for this.

5 Explain why:
a) The plants living in the swamp zone have long stems.
b) Water spiders are found where water lilies are growing.
c) Sticklebacks build their nests in the deep water zone.

It is impossible to count all the plants and animals that live in a particular habitat. Think how difficult it would be to count the plants in just a small section of field.

To make things easier we can use a method called **sampling**. A sample is a small part of a habitat that is studied very closely. If the sample is typical of the area, the distribution of plants and animals in the whole habitat will be similar to that in the sample. **Random sampling** makes sure that every part of a habitat has an equal chance of being chosen.

Counting plants and animals in a sample

This is best done using a wooden or metal frame called a **quadrat**. Quadrats are usually made so that they cover a known area of ground such as $0.25\,m^2$ or $1\,m^2$. Gridded quadrats are divided up into smaller quadrats by wires running from top to bottom and from side to side. This forms a sort of grid. Every square in the grid has the same area.

Quadrats can be used to see how often particular plant species occur across a habitat. This is called the **species frequency**. When the quadrat is lying on the ground you simply add up the number of squares that contain plants or animals of the same species. It doesn't matter how many plants or animals there are in each square. The final number is then calculated as a percentage of the total number of squares in the quadrat.

You can also use a quadrat to measure how much ground is covered by a species. This is called the **species cover**. You estimate how many squares would be filled up if you were able to move the plants or animals together.

Activities

1 Calculate the percentage frequency and percentage cover of plantain using the information in the quadrat above.
Which species is most frequent?
Which species covers most ground?
What is the relationship between the frequency and cover of a plant species and its size?

Sampling along a transect line

This method is best to measure population distribution in an area that is not the same all over. You may want to see how populations change as you move from a shaded part of a wood to an area which is in full sunlight.

A **transect line** is a piece of string or measuring tape stretched tightly between two poles across the survey area. The quadrat is then placed carefully in position along the line at regular intervals. These positions are called **stations**. The spaces between stations are usually 1 metre. This kind of transect is sometimes called a **belt transect** because a strip or belt of land is being surveyed.

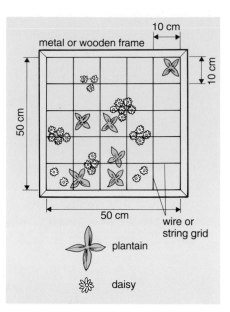

Worked example

The diagram shows a quadrat lying on the ground. In the quadrat are two different plants, daisy and plantain.

Frequency of daisy

Number of squares containing daisies $= {}^{13}/_{25}$
Frequency of daisies = **52%**

Cover of daisy

Total number of daisies in quadrat $= 26$
Number of daisies that would fit in one square $= 16$
Number of squares filled (approx.) $= {}^{26}/_{16}$
Cover of daisies = **6.5%**

Measuring plant distribution using the line transect method

Counting animals

Many animals are not always easy to see. If you are lucky you may be able to count some larger animals and birds, but usually you will only see footprints or droppings. However, we can use a number of methods to count animal populations.

Collection

A sweep net can be used to collect insects and spiders from the ground, field, and shrub layers. Animals can be collected from ponds and streams in a similar way. Once collected, the animals can be identified and kept in suitable containers until the count is finished. When all the animals have been counted they should be released safely back into their natural habitats.

Capture-recapture

This method is very useful if you want to count the number of individuals in one species. It involves capturing a group of animals, marking them in a way that does not harm them, and releasing them back into their habitat. After a day or so more animals are trapped at random. If the animals come from a large population the chance of collecting a marked animal the second time will be small. On the other hand, if you recapture all of your marked animals then you have probably seen the whole population!

You can estimate the size of the population by using the formula:

$$\text{estimated population} = \frac{\text{number of animals in first sample} \times \text{number of animals in second sample}}{\text{number of marked animals recaptured}}$$

There are some things that you need to be aware of when using this method.

- The habitat should have fixed boundaries.
- You must leave sufficient time before recapturing the animals: don't wait too long otherwise your marked animals may be dead.
- Marking methods must not affect the life of the animal. For example, it's no use marking snails in a way that makes them easily seen by birds.

Grazing wildebeest and zebra are easy to count in this area of the Serengeti in Tanzania.

Recording your results

It is very important to write down the results of your population counts as soon as you make them. Your notebook needs to be carefully organized so that no information is left out. With so much information to collect, it is very easy to forget something vital to your investigation.

Below is a page from a student's notebook. It shows information about the distribution of plant species in a wood. A line transect ran from a clearing into an area of deep shade. Quadrats were used at stations which were 1 metre apart.

species \ station	1	2	3	4	5	6	7	8	9	10	11	12	13	14	15	16	17
grass	100/80	100/70	60/40	60/40	50/20	40/20	20/20	20/20	10/10	10/10	10/10	10/10	10/10	10/10	10/10	10/10	10/10
primrose	0/0	0/0	20/20	50/40	50/40	80/40	80/40	40/20	20/10	0/0	0/0	0/0	0/0	0/0	0/0	0/0	0/0
fern	0/0	0/0	0/0	0/0	0/0	0/0	0/0	0/0	30/50	30/50	30/50	30/50	30/50	40/50	40/50	30/70	30/70
moss	20/10	20/10	10/10	10/10	10/10	20/30	20/30	30/20	40/20	40/20	40/20	40/20	40/20	40/20	40/20	40/20	40/20

Page from a field notebook

Anything which prevents growth in a population is called **environmental pressure**. There are a number of things which affect population growth. They can be divided up into two main groups.

Population-dependent pressures

These are due to the size of the population itself.

- A shortage of food, water, or oxygen affects all organisms. No living thing can survive without these necessities for life.
- Low levels of light severely limit the growth of plant populations. Without sufficient light, plants cannot photosynthesize. Without photosynthesis they die.
- A lack of space leads to overcrowding. This can affect the breeding habits of some animals, especially those like birds that have their own territories.
- The more individuals there are in a population, the closer they are to each other. If one becomes ill then the chances of others getting the disease are increased. If the disease is fatal, the population will decrease.
- Predators find it easier to catch prey if they are available in large numbers.

Population-independent pressures

These are things the population has no control over. They have the same effect whether the population is large or small.

- A sudden change in temperature may kill large numbers of organisms. For example, many birds die during a severe winter in Britain.
- Forest fires destroy not only large numbers of plants but also the animals that live in the forest habitat.
- Severe storms and floods wash away the homes of burrowing animals like rabbits. Plants covered with water for long periods also die.

Questions

1 List three things other than shortage of food, water, and oxygen that can cause the number of individuals in a population to fall.

2 What is the difference between population-dependent and population-independent pressures?

3 Suggest one other environmental pressure that a population has no control over.

4 In the 1950s the rabbit population in Britain was dramatically reduced by the disease myxomatosis. Suggest how the rapid spread of the disease could have taken place.

Large group of wild animals around a water hole

A cold winter can check population growth

The human population – the rule breaker

Most populations of plants and animals are controlled by predators, disease, seasonal changes in climate, and the availability of food. Populations frequently grow very fast or 'explode', and then suddenly crash when environmental pressures come into play.

Humans are at the top of food chains. They have little to fear from predators. Humans have the skill and knowledge to overcome many diseases. They build homes which protect them from the worst effects of changes in climate. Agricultural techniques have improved to the point where many countries produce more food than they need.

All these factors have resulted in the human population growing bigger and bigger, especially in recent times.

The graph shows the growth of the human population over a period of 500 000 years.

At the moment the human population is growing by about 1.5 million every week – that's 150 a minute!

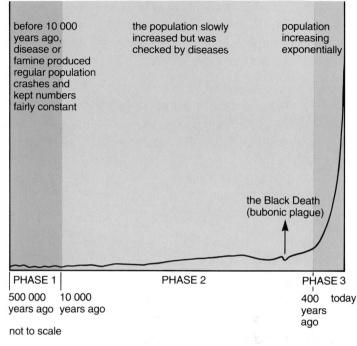

Human population growth

Patterns in human populations

In the developed countries of the world the growth of the human population is beginning to decline. In fact, in some Western European countries the population is no longer rising at all. The birth rate is being matched by the death rate.

As well as the total number of people in a population, it is useful to know the age and sex of the individuals in it. One way of showing this information is by a **population pyramid**.

A population pyramid is similar to the pyramid of numbers that you read about in Chapter 1. However, it usually involves much larger numbers. Each bar represents the number and sex of individuals in a particular age group. The youngest are at the bottom and the oldest at the top. Females are on the left and males are on the right. Two population pyramids are shown here.

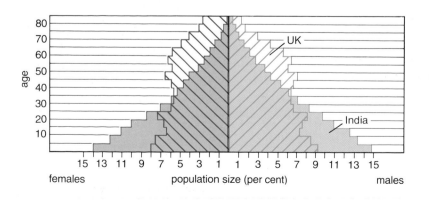

Questions

1 **a)** What is the difference between a population explosion and a population crash?
   b) List three things which could cause a population crash.

2 Explain briefly why the human population is not affected by environmental pressures as much as other populations.

3 Use the graph showing human population growth to answer the following questions.
   a) When was there no real increase in the human population?
   b) Why do you suppose the human population only rose slowly up to about 400 years ago?

107

Interactions between populations

A habitat is very rarely occupied by a single species of plant or animal. Communities contain many species, all of which interact with each other. There is competition for things like food, space, and shelter both within a species and between species.

One obvious relationship between two species is that between a **predator** and its **prey**. Predator–prey relationships play an important part in controlling populations. When a predator eats its prey it removes particular individuals from the population. These individuals are usually the sick or the old. Neither of these are of use to the species as a whole. Sick animals spread disease to others and the old use up valuable food supplies without breeding. This all sounds very heartless, but the future of a species depends on those healthy individuals that are able to breed successfully.

What happens when the young and healthy are eaten? Obviously the prey population begins to fall. If it falls too far the population of predators falls with it. Fewer predators means that fewer prey will be eaten. This allows the prey population to increase again. An example of this cycle is shown in the graph below.

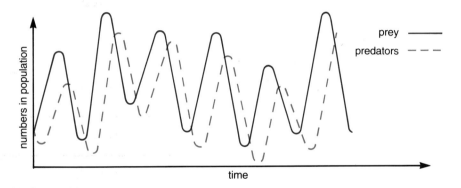

Notice that the number of predators is always lower than the number of prey and that the predator cycle closely follows that of the prey.

Questions

1 **a)** What is a predator–prey relationship?
b) Explain why such a relationship is important in controlling populations.

2 The graph opposite shows the effect of adding some *Paramecium* (single-celled animals) to a population of yeast.
a) What happens to the yeast population as soon as the *Paramecium* are added?
b) Why is there a time lag between the two population cycles?
c) If the *Paramecium* were removed, suggest what might happen to the yeast population.

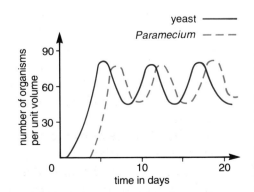

3 In what way are predator–prey relationships good for the evolution of species?

4 In what way are predator–prey relationships an example of negative feedback?

108

Messing about with food chains (1): DDT

One insecticide has done more than any other to enable farmers to grow more food crops. The name of this insecticide is dichlorodiphenyltrichloethane, known as **DDT**.

DDT was developed by scientists in the early 1940s. For many years DDT seemed to be the 'perfect insecticide'. It was used to kill off not only many of the insects that attacked food crops, but also those that live off humans such as lice and mosquitoes. However, scientists gradually became aware that DDT is not biodegradable. Levels of DDT build up in the soil. From the soil DDT can pass into streams and rivers and the oceans. It can therefore enter food chains. As it is passed from consumer to consumer it it stored in their fat layers, becoming more and more concentrated. The animals at the ends of food chains are eventually killed.

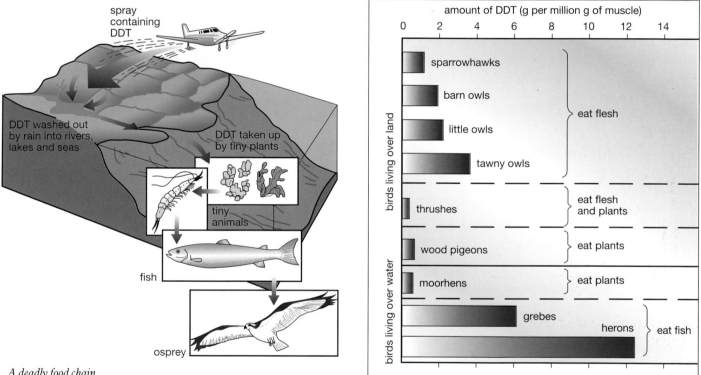

A deadly food chain.

Questions

1 In the 1960s scientists noticed that there was a fall in the numbers of certain types of birds of prey. They also noticed that this fall took place at about the same time as DDT was being widely used as an insecticide. As a result of these observations a large-scale survey was carried out. The survey showed the levels of DDT in predatory birds living in a number of different places. The results of the survey are shown in the chart.

   a) How much DDT was there in every million grams of grebe muscle?

   b) Which of the birds had about 2 grams of DDT in every million grams of its muscle?

   c) Suggest why carnivores that live near water have higher levels of DDT in their bodies than carnivores that live and feed over land.

Messing about with food chains (2): too much fertilizer

The development of new high-yield cereals has helped to meet the world's increasing demand for food. However, these new cereals need much more fertilizer than the older varieties. This has caused another serious problem for food chains.

Modern artificial fertilizers are soluble. Therefore much of the fertilizer used on the land gets washed away into nearby streams, rivers, and lakes. Most of the cereal produced in England comes from East Anglia. So it is not surprising that there are high concentrations of nitrogen and phosphorus in rivers in East Anglia, which come from land drainage.

The large amounts of nitrogen and phosphorus in the water encourage the growth of algae. The animals that feed on water plants cannot keep up with this rapid growth and soon the water becomes full of algae. As the algae die, poisonous substances are produced. This makes the water unfit for drinking and kills the animals living in it. Decomposers use up all the oxygen in the water, making it impossible for animals such as fish to breathe. Eventually the food web of the stream, river or lake is broken down.

Checking the effects of land drainage

It is possible to see what effect fertilizers have on water ecosystems by studying the kinds of animals living there. The chart shows the kinds of animals you might expect to find in water with different oxygen levels.

Questions

1 How do fertilizers get into waterways?

2 Explain briefly how fertilizers upset the balance of life in streams, rivers and lakes.

3 List three fish you would expect to see in a river with a high level of oxygen.

4 Roughly how much oxygen would you expect to find in a river that had no fish in it at all?

5 Warm water from power station cooling towers often runs into rivers. What effect does this warm water have on the oxygen content of a river *and* how will this affect the animals living in it?

amount of pollution	animals present	volume of oxygen (cm³/litre of water)	
		at 5 °C	at 20 °C
clean unpolluted water	stonefly nymph, mayfly nymph, salmon, trout, grayling, good coarse fishing	6.5-9.0	4.5-6
little pollution	caddis fly larvae, freshwater shrimp, good coarse fishing - trout rarely seen	6.0-6.5	4.0-4.5
some pollution	water louse, blood worm (ridge larvae), leech, roach, gudgeon, moderate to poor fishing	3.5-6.0	2.5-4.0
heavy pollution	sludge worm, cat-tailed maggot, no fish life	0-3.5	0-2.5

Natural resources

This chapter has shown how carbon, water and nitrogen pass through the Earth's ecosystem over and over again. These cycles maintain a balance in levels of the resources.

Energy, however, does not circulate in ecosystems. It enters from outside, flows through and eventually leaves, usually as heat.

The source of energy for our ecosystem is the Sun. Energy is 'trapped' by green plants during photosynthesis. The energy-rich products of this process are available for food or fuel. When the food is digested or the fuel is burnt, heat is produced which can be lost from our ecosystem to outer space.

With the dramatic rise in the human population in recent years the demand for natural resources has increased enormously. As a result we are in danger of upsetting the delicate balance of cycles and using up valuable sources of energy.

Some resources, like water . . .

. . . soil . . .

. . . and timber . . .

. . . are renewable, but they must be carefully managed. If we are too greedy and use them up too quickly we will create shortages. Demand should never exceed supply!

Other resources, like fossil fuels . . .

. . . uranium for nuclear energy . . .

. . . and species of animals and plants . . .

. . . are non-renewable – once used, they are gone forever.

Questions

1 List some renewable resources.

2 List some non-renewable resources.

3 What is the difference between a renewable and a non-renewable resource?

4 Suggest why we should refer to soil as being a renewable resource.

5 In Britain thousands of trees are cut down every day to make paper for newspapers and magazines.

Suggest **three** ways to make sure that we do not destroy our timber supply.

Pollution

As we use more of our natural resources we produce more waste. The build-up of waste leads to pollution of our environment. Anything which damages our environment is called a **pollutant**. Pollutants can cause illness and pollutants can kill!

Our local environment can be polluted with . . .

traffic noise and exhaust gases . . .   . . . litter . . .   . . . and cigarette smoke.

The search for more fossil fuels and minerals results in the pollution of . . .

water by oil . . .   . . . and pollution of land by slag heaps.

By-products of industrial processes include sulphur dioxide and compounds of lead, mercury and cyanide.

Sulphur dioxide dissolves in rain forming an acid. This 'acid rain' falls on land and in lakes far away from where it is first released, destroying trees and other life forms.

Lead, mercury and cyanide compounds are poisonous even in small quantities. They accumulate in the bodies of animals, especially fish, mainly because they are dumped into rivers that flow to the sea. People eating contaminated fish will suffer serious illness and probably die.

The effect of acid rain

The waste from nuclear power stations can give off radiation for thousands of years.

Questions

1   What is a pollutant?

2   List some pollutants of your school environment. Suggest how these could be controlled.

3   List some pollutants of your town environment. Suggest how these could be controlled.

4   Some farmers use pesticides to kill unwanted animals, and herbicides to kill unwanted plants. Why do you think they do this? What dangers could result from the use of such chemical poisons?

Questions

1 The diagram shows a food web for a pond ecosystem.

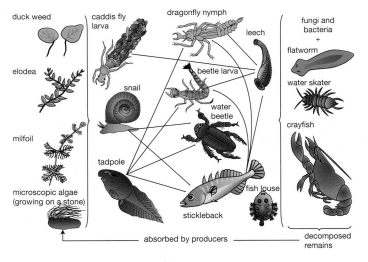

a) Write down two food chains ending at the water beetle.

b) Name:
  i) a primary consumer
  ii) a secondary consumer
  iii) a tertiary consumer
  iv) a scavenger
  v) a decomposer.

c) Suggest what might happen if all the water beetles were removed from the pond.

d) Give: i) one difference ii) one similarity between the parts played by scavengers and decomposers in keeping the pond ecosystem in balance.

2 The diagrams show four different pyramids of numbers.

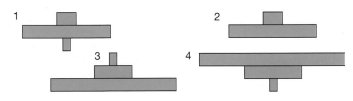

a) What does each pyramid represent?
b) Match each pyramid to the following:
  i) grass → antelope → lion
  ii) oak tree → caterpillar → sparrow
  iii) animals living in a balanced pond ecosystem
  iv) rose bush → greenfly → parasites of
    greenfly.
c) Briefly explain why pyramids of numbers can have different shapes, while pyramids of biomass have one basic shape.

3 Some students carried out a survey to find out the distribution of four plant species on some sand dunes. Their results are shown in the diagram.

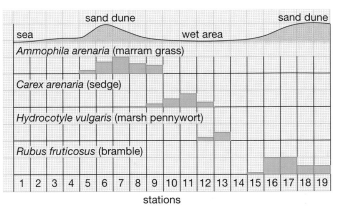

a) Describe the distribution of the plants across the survey area.
b) What is the percentage frequency of:
  i) *Ammophila arenaria* at station 5
  ii) *Hydrocotyle vulgaris* at station 13?

4 FIZZO lemonade is sold in plastic bottles. LEMO lemonade is sold in glass bottles.

make	**FIZZO**	**LEMO**
price	28p	38p
money back on bottle	—	10p
weight of bottle (full)	1100g	1500g

a) Using information from the table suggest *two* reasons why a shopper might choose to buy FIZZO lemonade rather than LEMO.
b) A person who wants to conserve the world's resources may choose to buy LEMO.
Suggest why.

113

What is biotechnology?

What are genes made of?

What is genetic engineering?

How can biotechnology help us?

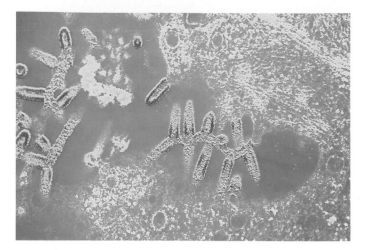

Biotechnology uses organisms that can only be seen with a microscope.

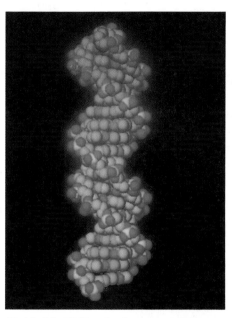

Model of the DNA molecule

Biotechnology has been around for thousands of years. People have been making bread and cheese, brewing wine and beer, and preserving food in vinegar for generations. Today we know a lot more about how these processes work.

Biotechnology is using cells to make useful things. It brings together the knowledge of the biologist and the skills of the technologist to provide food, medicines, and new materials for industry. It can also help to clear up much of the waste that pollutes our environment.

The biotechnologist may use whole cells or parts of cells such as DNA to control complex chemical reactions. Micro-organisms can be grown in vast quantities before being 'harvested' for food. They are also a source of important molecules such as antibodies.

By engineering genes, rare and expensive chemicals such as **insulin** can be made cheaply and efficiently.

Work with micro-organisms has to be carried out in sterile conditions.

Biotechnology past and present

Biotechnology probably began thousands of years ago with **fermentation**. This process was used to make bread, wine and beer, and vinegar. You probably know that fermentation is brought about by yeast. Yeast is a single-celled organism called a **microbe**. Other examples of microbes are **bacteria** and **viruses**. Bacteria were used to make yoghurt from milk and mould fungi were used to make cheese.

Of course we still use this 'old' biotechnology. In fact most modern work is based on the old methods. Modern biotechnology is on a much larger scale but it still depends on microbes.

Bread, beer, and cheese are all products of biotechnology.

Why use microbes?

Microbes grow quickly when given the right temperature and food supply. It is therefore easier to grow microbes in large quantities than to develop ways of growing plant and animal cells on their own. Also, microbe cells are relatively simple. This makes it easier for scientists to genetically engineer new microbes for specific jobs.

The biotechnology calendar

10 000	BC	Neolithic men and women ate fermented grain.
6000	BC	Babylonians used yeasts to make beer.
4000	BC	Egyptians used yeast to make bread dough rise.
2000	BC	The Chinese developed the fermentation process.
AD 1400		Distillation of wines and spirits was widespread.
AD 1500		Aztecs harvested algae from lakes for food.
1686		Leeuwenhoek made the first microscope and discovered microbes.
c. 1870		Pasteur proved that microbes were responsible for fermentation and for the decomposition of food.
c. 1890		Alcohol was first used as fuel.
1897		Buchner discovered that enzymes in yeast are responsible for converting sugar into alcohol.
1912		Microbes were first used in sewage works.
1912		Weizmann used bacteria to produce acetone (propanone) and butanol by fermentation.
1928		Fleming discovered penicillin.
1943		Avery provided evidence that DNA carries genetic information.
1944		Chain and Florey developed large-scale production of penicillin.
1953		Watson and Crick discovered the structure of DNA.
c. 1960		The genetic code was cracked.
1972		The first gene cloning was carried out.
1973		Brazil introduced its National Fuel Alcohol Programme.
1975		Kohler and Milstein first produced monoclonal antibodies.
1976		Guidelines on genetic engineering were drawn up.
1977		The first human gene was cloned.
1982		Human insulin was made by genetic engineering.
1987		Field trials of the first genetically engineered microbes started.
1988		Genetic 'fingerprinting' techniques were developed.
1997		Dolly, the first adult sheep clone.

Questions

1 Name two products that can be made by fermentation.

2 Some people say that biotechnology hasn't changed.
   a) Give one reason why they might be right.
   b) Give one reason why they might be wrong.

3 Give two reasons why biotechnologists use microbes.

DNA – it's all in the nucleus

All living things are made of **cells**. You may remember that the nucleus of a cell contains long, thread-like structures called **chromosomes**. Chromosomes carry bits of information called **genes**.

Genes instruct our bodies to make **proteins**. Proteins determine the shape of the body and how it behaves. Each gene controls the production of one particular protein.

Chromosomes and genes are made of **DNA** (*d*eoxyribo*n*ucleic *a*cid). DNA is a sort of plan that determines how the body is constructed. It is often called the 'blueprint for life' – every cell in an organism contains a copy of the blueprint. Notice how the DNA molecule is like a twisted ladder. This is called a **double helix**. The double helix is coiled up tightly on itself so that all DNA molecules can fit inside the cell nucleus.

The rungs of the ladder are made from pairs of **bases**. There are four kinds of bases. They have complicated names so we will use their initials.

Bases can only fit together in one way.

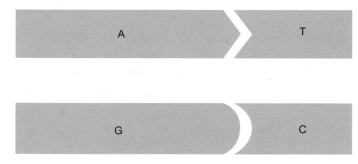

When cells divide the DNA first duplicates itself. A copy of the blueprint is passed from one generation to the next. This is the reason why we inherit characteristics from our parents. The diagram opposite shows how this duplication happens.

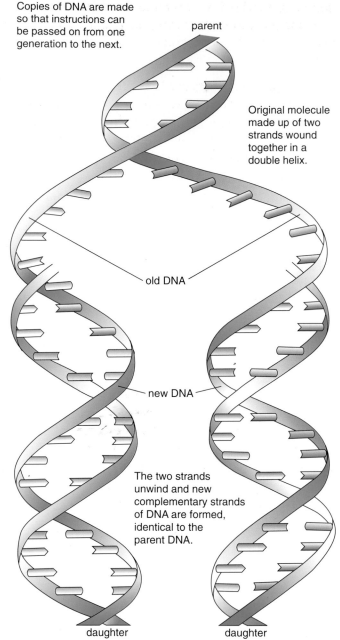

Copies of DNA are made so that instructions can be passed on from one generation to the next.

parent

Original molecule made up of two strands wound together in a double helix.

old DNA

new DNA

The two strands unwind and new complementary strands of DNA are formed, identical to the parent DNA.

daughter   daughter

DNA can make new strands identical to the old ones.

Questions

1 What are chromosomes?

2 What do genes make in our cells?

3 What does DNA stand for?

4 How would you describe the shape of the DNA molecule?

5 Why is DNA called the 'blueprint of life'?

6 Why do you suppose a large base is always paired with a small base in the DNA molecule? (*Hint:* think what would happen if two small bases were paired together.)

Genetic engineering involves removing genes from one type of cell and transferring them to another completely different cell. The techniques involved require a lot of precision and genetic engineers must be highly skilled.

Animal and plant products used in industry, agriculture, and medicine are often in short supply or very expensive. The genes controlling the production of these materials in animals and plants can be inserted into microbe cells. These genes then instruct the microbial cells to produce something they would not naturally do. Since microbes reproduce and grow at a rapid rate they produce the required materials in much greater quantities than the original animal or plant cells.

How is it done?

Cells contain thousands of genes. So the first step is to locate and then collect the required gene. Finding a gene is not easy, as you can imagine. The gene is removed from the chromosome by using special enzymes – like 'chemical scissors'.

Getting the gene into a microbial cell involves the use of **plasmids**. Plasmids are found in bacterial cells. They are small circles of DNA which are smaller than the single circular bacterial chromosome. Plasmids can move from one cell to another and make copies of themselves. By fixing the required gene into its correct position on a plasmid it can be introduced into a microbial cell. Once there it will be duplicated every time the microbial cell divides. Each of the new cells is called a **clone** because they all have the same genetic make-up. In just a few days there will be millions of cloned cells, each one carrying a copy of the original donated gene. This is called **gene cloning**.

All that remains is to persuade the microbial cell to begin making the appropriate product and then devise an economical method of collecting it.

Questions

1 What is genetic engineering? Explain the process briefly.

2 Why have genetic engineering techniques been developed?

3 Why are microbes used in genetic engineering?

4 Why do you suppose enzymes are called 'chemical scissors'?

5 What are plasmids? Give two reasons why plasmids are used in genetic engineering.

6 What is a clone?

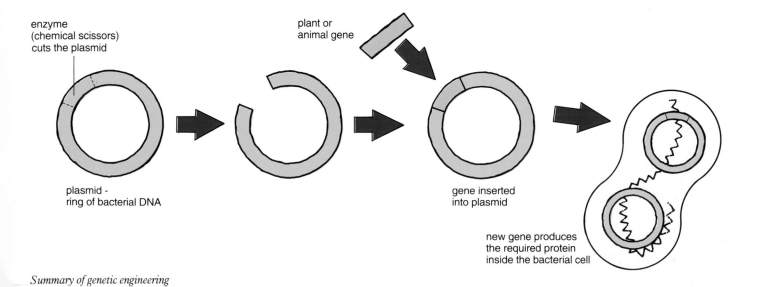

enzyme (chemical scissors) cuts the plasmid

plant or animal gene

plasmid - ring of bacterial DNA

gene inserted into plasmid

new gene produces the required protein inside the bacterial cell

Summary of genetic engineering

Microbes – new sources of food

Although the thought of eating microbes may not be very pleasant, we do in fact eat quite a few. Cheese and yoghurt contain microbes, bread and beer are made using microbes, and yeast extract is almost pure microbes! Algae, fungi, and bacteria can all be used directly as sources of food.

Algae are simple plants that live in water. They contain a lot of protein, vitamins, and minerals. Hundreds of years ago the Aztecs collected and ate an alga called *Spirulina maxima*. It didn't have much taste but it was a valuable source of nutrients.

Today food scientists are once again showing interest in *Spirulina* as a food. In hot countries where cereal crops are difficult to cultivate, *Spirulina* is grown in long plastic ponds.

Fungi such as mushrooms have been eaten for centuries. Recently, however, attention has been directed to a mould fungus called *Fusarium*. *Fusarium* contains about 45% protein and 13% fat – about the same as the protein: fat ratio of meat. The big advantage that *Fusarium* has over meat is that it contains a lot of fibre and is cholesterol free.

Fusarium will grow on any material containing carbohydrate such as potatoes, starch, or wheat. These are relatively cheap. Afterwards the fungus can be collected and used to make artificial meat. You will find this fungal protein in a number of products at your local supermarket. Look out for it on the label – it is called **mycoprotein**.

A bacterium called *Methylophilus methylotrophus* grows well on methanol. Methanol can be made quite cheaply from natural gas. Mineral salts, ammonia, a plentiful supply of air, and a suitable temperature are essential for successful growth of the bacteria.

When removed from the ethanol the bacteria are dried. The dried bacterial cells contain protein. The commercial name for this protein is **Pruteen**. As in the production of mycoprotein, conditions for Pruteen manufacture must be sterile. In fact, very few other microbes will grow in methanol so there is little risk of contamination.

A **continuous culture** process is used in Pruteen production. This means that as bacteria are removed they are replaced with similar amounts of starting materials.

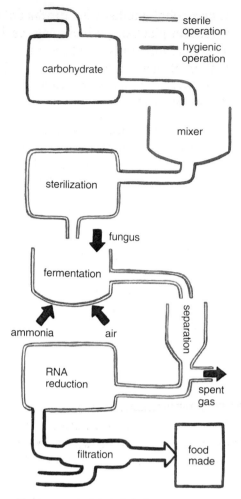

Making mycoprotein in industry

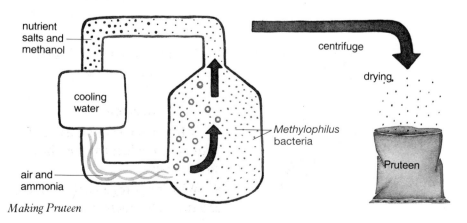

Making Pruteen

Questions

1 Name three foods that contain microbes.

2 What nutritional value is there in the alga *Spirulina*?

3 How are meat and the mould fungus *Fusarium* **a**) similar **b**) different?

4 What three things are needed for the successful growth of *Methylophilus* bacteria?

5 Why must the conditions for making mycoprotein and Pruteen be sterile?

6 What is a continuous culture process? What do you think is the advantage of such a process?

Biotechnology and fuel: flammable gases

Like alcohol, methane is a product of a natural process. It is produced whenever plant and animal remains decompose in the absence of oxygen. There are lots of places where this could happen, such as in the mud at the bottom of stagnant ponds. You may have seen bubbles of methane gas rising to the surface of the water. Don't try lighting it though, methane is a flammable gas!

Methane is produced on a much larger scale inside the Earth's crust. For millions of years bacteria have been breaking down organic material into methane gas. Today we can drill deep into the Earth to extract it. North Sea gas or 'natural gas' is methane.

Like ethanol, methane is produced by fermentation. It is made by bacteria feeding on organic waste rather than yeast on sugar.

Biotechnologists are already considering the uses of methane-producing bacteria. The bacteria could provide us with a renewable source of natural gas. There are plenty of raw materials around, including unwanted waste. Household and farmyard sewage, industrial waste, and rubbish provide ideal materials for use in fermenters. Some scientists have even suggested using fast-growing seaweeds. These could be grown in huge floating grids in the sea.

Some farms and sewage works use methane-powered generators to produce their own electricity. Cattle produce the raw materials on farms. In the sewage works it comes from us. The methane is produced in large closed tanks called **digesters**. It is important that the temperature inside the digester is kept at about 35°C because this is an ideal temperature for the bacteria.

Digester

How do digesters work?

Methane production is slow and is quite a complicated process. There are two stages:

1 Acid formation – animal and human waste contains acid-forming bacteria. These bacteria break down the waste into simple organic acids.

2 Methane formation – the organic acids are broken down by methane-forming bacteria. Methane gas is produced.
The sludge left at the bottom of the digester is removed and used as fertilizer.

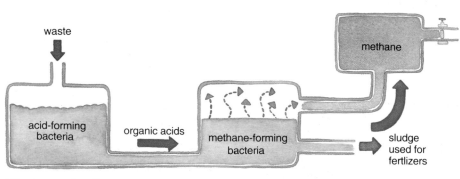

What happens in a digester

Questions

1 How is methane produced?

2 Name a place where methane is produced naturally.

3 Why do you think North Sea gas is called natural gas?

4 Give **a)** one similarity **b)** one difference between the production of ethanol and that of methane.

5 List four raw materials that could be used in methane production.

6 What are digesters?

7 What effect would the use of hydrogen as a fuel have on the environment?

8 Why is hydrogen not produced as a fuel at the moment?

Biotechnology and health

Biotechnology and health have been closely linked for many years. It was in the middle of the nineteenth century that Louis Pasteur and Robert Koch first discovered that microbes were the cause of most common diseases. The production of useful medicines such as vaccines and antibiotics is the job of the biotechnologist.

A **vaccine** is a liquid containing dead or weakened microbes. Vaccines work by stimulating the natural defences of the body. Antibodies are produced by white blood cells every time microbe cells enter the body. These antibodies destroy the invading microbes and disease symptoms are removed.

Unfortunately there are still some diseases for which there are no vaccines. Those such as the common cold and mumps are not so serious because, given time, the body can cure itself. However, a much more serious example is AIDS. There is no known cure for AIDS.

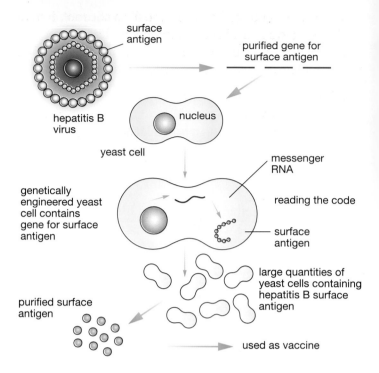

Producing a vaccine by genetic engineering. A problem facing scientists is finding a way to produce large amounts of vaccine quickly. Recently success has been achieved with the production of a vaccine against the serious liver disease hepatitis B. This is how it is done.

Antibiotics destroy bacteria. It was Alexander Fleming who, in 1928, discovered the first antibiotic. It was called **penicillin**. The name penicillin comes from the mould fungus *Penicillium notatum*. Fleming discovered penicillin almost by accident. By mistake, the mould infected some bacterial cultures he had been working on. Instead of throwing the cultures away Fleming looked at them and noticed there were no bacteria around the blue-green mould. The mould was giving off a substance that prevents bacterial growth. This substance was penicillin.

How do antibiotics work?

Penicillin is not the only antibiotic. There are a number of others including **cephalosporin** and **streptomycin**. It is important that new antibiotics are developed because bacteria can become **resistant** to them. When penicillin was first used many major bacterial infections could be cured. However, some types of bacteria that were once easily killed by penicillin are now able to survive. Mutations have occured in some bacteria making them resistant to penicillin. The resistant bacteria have survived – they have been favoured by **natural selection**.

Cephalosporin comes from the fungus *Cephalosporium*. Fortunately it is effective against penicillin-resistant bacteria. Penicillin and cephalosporin work in the same way – by stopping bacteria building a cell wall.

Streptomycin works in a different way. It stops bacteria making protein by interrupting the reading of the genetic code carried by messenger RNA.

Questions

1 What is a vaccine?

2 Name **a**) one disease that can **b**) one disease that cannot be prevented by a vaccine.

3 Briefly describe a vaccine that can be produced by genetic engineering. Why is this technique an important step in vaccine production?

4 **a**) Who discovered penicillin? **b**) What kind of organism produces it? **c**) What colour is this organism?

5 **a**) Name two other antibiotics. **b**) Briefly explain how they work.

6 How can we help reduce bacterial resistance to antibiotics?

1 Josie's pet dog, Skip, became ill so she took him to the vet. Skip had a bacterial infection. The vet prescribed some antibiotics. She told Josie to give Skip two tablets every day after meals for the next ten days.

After four days Skip seemed much better so Josie stopped giving him the tablets. Unfortunately Skip became very ill again a few days later.

Josie started giving Skip the tablets again but this time they did not make Skip better.

Once again Skip was taken to the vet. The vet was very annoyed with Josie for not completing the course of antibiotics. She gave Josie some different antibiotics for Skip. This time Josie made sure she gave Skip all the tablets as instructed. Skip got better.

a) What are antibiotics?
b) What do they do?
c) Explain why Skip got better after the first four days of treatment.
d) Suggest why Skip became ill again and only recovered when different antibiotics were given.

2 The diagram shows a pressure cycle fermenter used by ICI to make Pruteen.

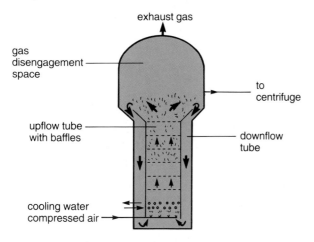

a) What does the compressed air do?
b) What is the job of the cooling water pipes?
c) Why do you suppose there is an exhaust valve?
d) Why do you think the fermenter is called a pressure cycle fermenter?
e) Why does the mixture rise in the centre tube?
f) ICI claims the pressure cycle fermenter is more sterile than fermenters fitted with stirrers.
Why is it important for the fermenter to be sterile?
g) Explain how a centrifuge is used to remove the product.

3 The diagram shows a summary of the processes involved in genetic engineering.

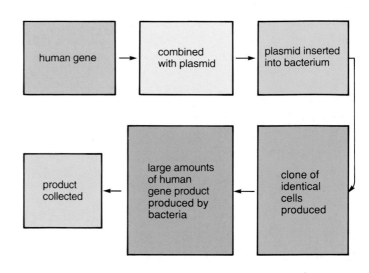

a) What is i) a gene   ii) a plasmid   iii) a clone?
b) List the four main stages in genetic engineering.
c) Give two reasons why microbes such as bacteria are used in genetic engineering.
d) Genetic engineering is used to produce human insulin. Why is insulin important in the body?
e) What happens to a person who cannot produce enough insulin of their own?
f) Why is it better to produce human insulin by genetic engineering than to use the insulin from large animals such as cattle?

4 Farmer Stone generates his own electricity using a methane-powered generator. He collects all the manure from his cows and puts it into a large tank. Inside the tank the manure is decomposed by bacteria and methane gas is produced.

a) What does **decomposed** mean?
b) Give two reasons why methane can be used as a fuel.
c) The tank into which Farmer Stone puts the cow manure is called a **digester**. Why is this?
d) Give one precaution that Farmer Stone should take when making methane gas.
e) What use could Farmer Stone make of the sludge left behind in the tank?
f) Suggest how Farmer Stone   i) can save money   ii) can help to protect the environment by making and using his own methane gas.

Index